D1229134

Reviews for Rural Hospital Renaissance

"The patient drive-by, silent but deadly. Excellent information to keep that from happening. The differentiator of a 5 Star hospital is a DNA of empathy, kindness and compassion, an amazing recipe for success in rural hospitals."

Brock Slabach, Senior Vice President for Member Services, NRHA - National Rural Health Association

"If stories of hospital closures, declining life expectancy and lack of access and coverage have got you down, Brian's book that challenges all of us to rethink and transform culture and experience, could be just what the doctor ordered."

John Henderson, CEO / President Texas Organization of Rural & Community Hospitals (TORCH)

"*Brian Lee is able to dive into the core of what builds a quality hospital. In a world that is centered around patient satisfaction and quality controls, this books highlights the major topics that health care executives can target to become a 5 Star health care system.*"

Ryan Kelly, Executive Director
Mississippi Rural Health Association

"*Rural Hospital Renaissance provides practical steps for improving the patient experience, and achieving excellence within a rural hospital.*"

Alan Morgan, MPA
Chief Executive Officer
National Rural Health Association

"*After reviewing the Rural Hospital Renaissance Draft, I found the information to be key to anyone who may need guidance in making their organization better in so many ways. By empowering the staff and having everyone take ownership in an organization helps morale and the clients being served. Working in public health, it is imperative to be attentive to the needs of others. Some people need guidance within an organization, some may need to be spoken to in a sincere manner and others may need for someone to just listen to them. Regardless, as public servants, we must always be attentive and show compassion to our customers/clients*".

Sherry Johnson, MBA, CPM, Bureau Chief,
Arkansas Office of Rural Health
and Primary Care Section Chief
Center for Health Protection

"This is what we need now. The key to many things in life including health care is the ability to act with kindness. It is the highest honor to serve the community and through our service we must simply remember to be kind. Rural Hospital Renaissance provides excellent practical solutions to increase a patient focused culture."

Michelle Mills, Chief Executive Officer
Colorado Rural Health Center The
State Office of Rural Health

"Practical ideas that can be successfully implemented in limited resource environments."

Mary Sheridan, Bureau Chief
Bureau of Rural Health and Primary Care
Division of Public Health | Idaho
Department of Health and Welfare

"The value and knowledge expressed in Rural Hospital Renaissance goes right to the heart of why hospitals exist. Sometimes all of us get wrapped up in regulations and the day to day challenges of running hospitals and forget to go back to the core of why we are all here. The tenants outlined in this book are the path to where we all want to be."

Rodney D. Smith M.B.A, FACHE
Vice President/Administrator
SIH/Herrin Hospital

"An invaluable tool for any rural health care administrator. Brian will take you through step by step what is needed to overcome the many obstacles faced by rural providers and inspire you along with way."

Margaret Vaughn,
Executive Director
Illinois Rural Health Association,

"If you wonder why you are not taking care of your primary market as they drive elsewhere and want to be a 5 star organization ALWAYS - this is the only book you need. If you want a roadmap to maintaining employee engagement and delivering 5 star care, read this book and then be relentless in implementation."

Ada Bair, CEO
UnityPoint Health-Memorial Hospital
Hancock County Senior Services, Illinois

"Brian Lee's book, Rural Hospital Renaissance, is timely and reinforces the concept of front line staff having intentional and positive engagement with patients. Management understanding and demonstrating support to every aspect of patient and family contact will have the best chance of organizational survival. Simply organizing with thoughtful actions the concept of people taking care of family, neighbors, and friends. Hospital staff are constantly on stage and watched while performing every aspect of their training and job. They need to remember that even during difficult and emotional interactions".

Don Kelso
Executive Director
Indiana Rural Health Association

"Brian Lee has given us invaluable insight into what drives patient loyalty. The patient experience is the only thing that matters."

Harold Courtois, CEO
Memorial Health System
Abilene, Kansas

"The game changer in this book is that we learned we were playing the wrong game. While well intentioned, we were trying to drive change from the top down. However to achieve a real and lasting change, you must engage and empower front line staff to execute your rural hospital renaissance. Our financial and quality turnaround started once we began utilizing the tools Brian outlines in the book. We had these tools taught to frontline staff by their peers, not our managers. We were able to win (engage, transform, and grow) once we changed games".

Michael Slusher, MHA, FACHE
Community Chief Executive Officer
Middlesboro ARH, Kentucky

"I find in reading it great information every CEO and manager should understand that is beneficial for any size hospital in the United States. A practical and easy way to implement changes that will impact health care in these changing times. Why not implement these tools? Otherwise, you can expect to be left behind and wondering where did I go wrong. Where did all my patients go and why?"

Margaret Brockman, RN, MSN
Administrator, Office of Rural Health
Division of Public Health
Nebraska Office of Rural Health

"Patient centric care is a goal every organization should aspire to provide, but getting there requires a road map that everyone can follow. Rural Hospital Renaissance provides the basics to help any organization begin the journey".

Virginia A. Razo
Chief Executive Officer
Curry Health Network, Oregon

"Brian Lee dives headfirst into the issue of rural hospital transformation in his book Rural Hospital Renaissance by providing easy to implement solutions that speak right to the heart of the matter. His focus on transforming into a 5 Star health care system with the patient experience at the center, provides health care executives with a blueprint for transformation."

Rebecca Jolley, MBA
Executive Director
Rural Health Association of Tennessee

Brian Lee

Rural Hospital Renaissance

Achieve a breatkthrough in the patient experience to transform the future from decline and survival, to growth and revival.

www.savingruralhospitals.com

Lee, Brian

Rural Hospital Renaissance
Achieve a breatkthrough in the patient experience to transform the future from decline and survival to growth and revival.

ISBN 978-0921328094

All rights reserved. No part of this publication may be reproduced, stored in a retrieval system or transmitted in any form or by any means, electronic, mechanical, photocopying, recording or otherwise without the prior permission of the publisher or in accordance with the provisions of the Copyright, Designs and Patents Act 1988 or under the terms of any licence permitting limited copying issued by the Copyright Licensing Agency.

© 2019 Mastery Publishing Co.
3rd Edition 2019
1. Hospital/Health care
2. Customer Service
3. Business Improvement

Published by:
    Mastery Publishing Co.
    (a division of Custom Learning Systems Group Ltd.)
    200-2133 Kensington Road NW
    Calgary, Alberta, Canada T2N 3R8

Printed and bound in TN, U.S.A. by InstantPublisher

Acknowledgements

I gratefully acknowledge Roger for his contributions, expertise, and commitment. Roger joined Custom Learning System in January 2001 as a speaker and trainer. He brought humor, art and above all, Service Excellence to everything that he touched. Roger Irvin Brugraff July 9, 1941 - July 26, 2019. Thank you Roger, you will be missed.

Roger Burgraff, Ph.D.
Co-Author

Brian Lee CSP
Healthcare's "Mr. Engagement"

Profile of an author and
world-class professional speaker

Brian Lee CSP

Brian Lee is the founder and CEO of Custom Learning Systems Group and the HealthCare Service Excellence Conference.

He has been awarded the prestigious designation CSP (Certified Speaking Professional) by the National Speakers Association.

With headquarters in Calgary, Canada, Brian has lead his team of training professionals for 35 years, focused exclusively on hospitals and health care.

34 of their clients have earned regional and national awards for world-class patient experience, employee and physician engagement.

Brian has personally trained and consulted over 300 Critical Access Hospitals throughout the nation over the past 20 years.

For two consecutive years, the International Customer Service Association rated Brian the #1 Customer Service Speaker in the world.

Brian is the author of 8 books, including "Keep Your Nurses and Healthcare Professionals for Life™" and "Satisfaction Guaranteed™"

He is also the author of the acclaimed HCAHPS Breakthrough Leadership Series™ webinars and the Everyone's a Caregiver™ Micro-Webinar System.

In the past 35 years, he has travelled 5,000,000 miles to speak more than 3,840 times. He's spoken in every state and province in North America, and in 16 countries worldwide.

Put Brian Lee to work for your next conference or meeting.
1.800.667.7325 • Keynotes • Seminars • Consulting • Coaching

Rural Hospital Renaissance

BRIAN LEE CSP

Table of Contents

A Blueprint For Success

In Florence, Italy, at the close of the Middle Ages, in the 14th Century, a momentous event occurred. Spreading throughout Europe, a relatively sudden and pervasive renewal of learning and culture took place. This movement is referred to as "The Renaissance." ("rebirth"). Universities sprang up; art and literature began to flourish. This period spawned such giants as Leonardo da Vinci, Michelangelo, Erasmus, Donatello and Raphael to name a few. The term "Renaissance," is used today to highlight revitalization or renewal and can be applied to individuals, and institutions or organizations, including hospitals.

A cultural Renaissance in health care is currently taking place. There is a renewed focus on maximizing the patient experience. This renewal is accomplished through empowered frontline engagement led by total management engagement. The magic consists of building positive connections between patients and frontline staff as well as positive connections between management and staff. It is nothing less than achieving a breakthrough in the patient experience to transfer the future of health care from decline and survival to growth and revival.

My mission for the book is to empower readers as patient relationship experts to implement a blueprint to become a Rural 5 Star Hospital of Choice.

To assist you in that journey, I have included two invaluable tools:

- Addendum C
  A self scoring Rural Hospital Assessment tool that will enable you to complete your very own "Survival Index", as a valuable benchmark in your journey.

- Addendum D
  A study of HCAHPS Best Practices in High Performing Critical Access Hospitals authored by StratisHealth.

This 100% relevant research provides an extraordinary guide to rural hospital leaders wishing to improve and I extend my enthusiastic gratitude to StratisHealth for their authorship and the permission to reprint.

CHAPTER 1

Two Ways To Grow Market Share

There are only two ways to grow your market share:

#1   Provide New Services

#2   Word Of Mouth Advertising

There are obviously many constraints to developing new services. So, it's more useful to turn our attention to "word of mouth." How important are word of mouth recommendations to you?

Have you ever gone to a movie based on a word of mouth recommendation? I often go to movies based on recommendations from friends. It's the same for books or articles to read. How about selecting a handyman? In the face of no evidence to the contrary, we all tend to follow word of mouth recommendations from family and friends and what we find on the internet. How much more important is this when selecting a hospital or residential facility for yourself or a loved one?

In the world of health care there are at least 16 websites that are available for access by our patients. In other words there are a lot of ways they can check on our service:

- www.besthospitaladvisor.com
- www.caring.com
- www.caredash.com
- www.google.com
- www.healthgrades.com
- www.ratehospitals.com
- www.ratemds.com
- www.topdocs.com
- www.wellness.com
- www.vitals.com
- www.webmd.com
- www.yelp.com
- www.yellowpages.com
- www.zocdoc.com
- www.whynotthebest.org
- www.topdoctors.com

The ratings from these sites provide transparency of the customer experience in health care institutions for everyone to see. More and more people are consulting these sites to guide their decision making.

Yet, with all of this internet technology available …

"People influence people. Nothing influences people more than a recommendation from a trusted friend. A trusted referral influences people more than the best broadcast message. A trusted referral is the Holy Grail of advertising."
– Mark Zuckerberg, CEO, Facebook

In rural areas especially, patients, neighbours, friends, and family offering recommendations is all that matters when selecting a health care institution.

Remember – Advertising will not bring back people who don't like you.

Having placed about one million dollars of advertising in a year, I was once asked how much of it works. I replied, "About half." I was asked which half and I had to reply that I didn't know. But what I did know is that recommendations from a satisfied customer or patient do work.

"A brand is no longer what we tell the consumer it is. It is what the consumers tell each other it is."
– Scott Cook, CEO and
co-founder of Intuit

Here are some startling numbers: "84% of consumers say they either completely or somewhat trust recommendations from family and friends about patient services."

And… "88% of people trust online reviews by other consumers as much as they trust recommendations from personal contacts." *(www.getambassador.com)*

In these days of social media exposure, your service is fishbowl transparent. People are beginning to trust what they find online as much or even more than personal recommendations.

What are your patients reading about your hospital?

"Are your patients and their families telling their story of their experiences the way we hope they will?"

Ken Blanchard and Sheldon Bowls,
"Raving Fans"

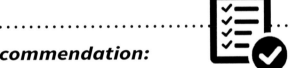

Recommendation:

Set a personal example to engage and influence everyone to ensure that no patient leaves your institution without experiencing a kind, compassionate experience.

## CHAPTER 2

You Have 100% Control

While your patients are with you, you have 100% control over your influence on them.

NOTE: when they leave, you have 0% influence!

Let's face it, when patients are with us, they notice us, they hear us and observe all of our behaviours. After all, what else have they got to do? We are a walking/talking drama occurring on the stage of their room. As the song goes, *"Every breath you take, every move you make, every bond you break, and every step you take they are watching you."* At all times we are under a patient's surveillance and scrutiny.

Think back to a time when you were hospitalized. Were you not hyper-aware of all the actions of people who entered your room and what they said? When we're hospitalized, most of us feel vulnerable, bored, scared, and dependent on others for everything. It's inevitable and understandable that we notice everything going on around us. Being hospitalized is an intensely personal experience. I vividly remember the few inpatient experiences I've had. I'll bet you remember yours too.

Not only are patients watching, but they are making conscious and unconscious judgments about their health care givers. It is estimated that we are being judged by over 200 attributes, mostly unconscious but some conscious. And based on these judgments patients are evaluating their experience of us. Do we listen? Are we compassionate? Are we thorough? Do we seem indifferent? They aren't able to evaluate our technical skills, but they readily know when we are kind and compassionate.

What were some of the judgments you made while you were a patient? One patient, Mr. B, was adamant that he was not being listened to by his nurses and the PT had him attached to a device that kept his leg moving after a knee replacement. The patient did not think the machine was doing what it was supposed to do. With only a cursory look, these health care professionals said, "There is nothing wrong with the machine, it is working fine." Finally, Mr. B took independent action and insisted upon talking to a nursing supervisor who wisely did listen, inspected the device more carefully, and altered it so it worked properly. Leadership finally came through in the form of good listening and taking action.

The point: The patient experiences cultural renaissance through the actions of empowered frontline engagement.

What differentiates a 4 Star hospital from a 5 Star hospital is a DNA of empathy, kindness, and compassion.

Creating a
Relationship Centered
Culture of Healing Kindness

Recommendation

Implement hospital-wide actions to ensure patients have a kind, positive experience under your care.

Brian Lee

## CHAPTER 3

A Renaissance of Compassionate Care

Achieve a breakthrough in the patient experience by creating a Renaissance of Compassionate Care. By doing so, you can transform the future of your hospital from decline and survival, to growth and revival.

Principles of Compassionate Care

1. The "Drive-By" Factor

2. Six Vital Questions

3. What Differentiates You?

4. The Four "Must-Haves"

The guiding agenda to achieve our mission has four critical elements. Implementation of these will fulfil our goal of a hospital Renaissance. Let's preview each of these and then explore them in detail in the subsequent chapters.

1. **Calculate the "Drive-By" factor** (Chapter 4)
   How valuable would it be to know how much business you're losing when patients drive by your hospital to go to another facility? How much of this potential business is retrievable? What do you have to do to substantially reduce the drive-by factor? How important is word of mouth advertising in this regard? We can reduce the drive-by factor.

2. **Ask the six vital questions your team needs to answer** (Chapter 5)
   Questions stimulate thinking. In chapter five we tackle each of these six vital issues. Together, the answers represent how we come to understand and appreciate how our service is evaluated. To develop the Cultural Renaissance we're striving for, we need to know the answers to these questions.

3. **Consider the only differentiation that matters** (Chapter 6)
   What makes our hospital unique? How do we become the health care facility of choice? Surveys, empirical studies and tons of anecdotal evidence provide the obvious answer. Implementing this differentiating factor is inexpensive, takes virtually no time, is easy and most importantly – is effective.

4. **Generate the four "Must-Haves" to become the hospital or health care facility your patient will unreservedly recommend** (Chapter 7)

What do you think the four "must-haves" might be? You might be surprised by the typical answers to this question. How do the typical answers differ from reality? Shortly, you will see that the answers are absurdly simple yet profound.

Our goal for our readers:

Develop an implementable blueprint to be 5 Star.

5 Star Experience defined:

"Consistently meet or manage patient's expectations with kindness care, everywhere."

To accomplish our mission will take a strong commitment leading to some simple but profound changes in leadership and frontline behaviours. Some may fear that this must require a lot of additional work. That is not true. It will require incorporating practical, easy-to-do modifications to what we already do as a matter of routine.

The Patient Star Struck Factor

RED ZONE   3 Stars = patients pack,

> *Leadership Engagement,*
> *and HCAHPS Skills*

YELLOW ZONE   4 Stars = are somewhat slack,

> *Frontline Engagement*
> *and the License to*
> *Please bundle*

GREEN ZONE   5 Stars = keep and wins them back

> *Patient Engagement*
> *= Word of mouth*

Recommendation:

Implement the four Principles of Compassionate Care.

## CHAPTER 4

The "Drive-By" Factor

What do we mean by the "Drive-By."

It is estimated that a range from 4 to 15 million dollars of business drives past your rural health care institution at their inconvenience to go to your competitors for the same services you offer. *(These numbers are based on information provided in Economic Impact Statement and AHD.com).* We need to consider the issue of developing customer loyalty to minimize or avoid the dreaded drive-by.

There are three attributes of customer loyalty in health care:

1. Patients report that they are very satisfied with their hospital experience. This means in the scoring guidelines that patients rated the hospital 4 out of 4 or 9 or 10 out of 10.

2. Patients report that they would definitely return to your facility. *(People tend to go to the hospital an average of 5 times in a lifetime.)*

3. Patients report that they would definitely recommend your facility to others.

Now for the bad news and the good news:

The bad news is that only a third of the patients would say "yes" to all three of these attributes. This means that two-thirds of your patients are at risk to your competitors.

The good news is that two-thirds of your competitor's patients are at risk to you, if you offer a meaningful experience for them to come back.

We know, for example, that happy people will tell five others about their experiences, unhappy people will tell 12 others. Unhappy mothers like mine will tell the whole world. *(Negative word of mouth advertising is the price we pay for rudeness, indifference, or uncaring)*. This has a powerful impact on the population we serve. We know some dissatisfied patients who will tell everyone they meet about their bad experiences *(for years)* while they were patients. Health care institutions cannot afford this kind of bad word of mouth advertising which will exacerbate the "drive-by" factor. If you are intent on losing business, create an atmosphere in which patients are poorly treated.

Vital Facts: OLD WORLD

*   *"A happy patient will tell 5 others, an unhappy patient will tell 12"* – Source HARP

- An unhappy mother will tell 250!

We've all seen the stories on the internet of consumers unhappy with their treatment. You may be familiar with Dave Carroll's true story. He was flying on United Airlines from Nova Scotia through Chicago to Nebraska to perform. As the plane landed in Chicago, he saw from his window the baggage handlers throwing around his $3,500.00 guitars like footballs. They were damaged beyond repair. He complained, and they got mad at him for complaining. He never did get reimbursed. So, he wrote the song "United Breaks Guitars" and put it on You Tube. It went viral. Guess how many hits it's had to date?

"*United Breaks Guitars*" – *Dave Carroll*

By the way, you may be interested to know that this video has been viewed 17,738,199 and that number is still growing!

I hate to continue with another United story but we all saw the doctor physically dragged off a United flight kicking and screaming who suffered broken teeth in the episode. He sued and won damages of two million dollars.

Think of the negative impact on a business when huge numbers of consumers are exposed to these kind of negative customer accounts.

Yelp commentaries about service *(including health care services)* are becoming a "go to" source for people to check out what customers say about their experiences with companies and other institutions *(including health care facilities).*

We create customer loyalty by providing extraordinary service. Building this kind of loyalty is crucial to the continued growth and revival of our hospital.

Having calculated our "drive-by" factor, what must we do to implement a strategy to maintain and increase our customer base? Improving the "drive-by" factor means creating a reputation through extraordinary service that acts like a magnet for people to choose your facility over your competitors.

Recommendations:

1. Engage everyone using the guidelines above to regain part or all of that drive-by revenue.

2. Let's begin with the six vital questions that must be answered. *(Remember: questions stimulate thinking which often leads to change.)*

## CHAPTER 5

Six Vital Questions

Gathering information to guide the change in the patient's hospital experience.

Six vital questions your team needs to consider.

Vital question #1

Why won't patients tell you how they honestly feel about you and the care they're receiving while under your control?

You can probably guess some of the answers to this one. Patients *(especially the elderly)* may want to avoid a "hassle," they don't think they're important enough to disturb you, they may be in pain or under the influence of drugs, they are not sure how to phrase their concerns, and they may be afraid of repercussions and so on. Some of us refrain from complaining about food in a restaurant because we're afraid of what will happen to the food when it is returned from the kitchen.

We often hear from nurses who have been rounding that, *"The patients love us."* But sometimes the patients don't give their honest evaluations until they feel safe at home.

It is true that the way we see ourselves may not be the way the patients and families see us.

For example, we may believe we are being efficient, they may see us as abrupt or uncaring. While we feel we are paying attention to the patient, our lack of eye contact may indicate that we are not listening.

Our perception = deception

Nurses have often reported to us that when you ask a patient, for example, "How are things going?" How do patients respond? Usually, they say, "fine," but don't really mean it. We need patients to open up and be honest with us. How do we do that?

The solution is to do our best to be empathetic, i.e. putting ourselves in our patient's place. And let them hear our empathy. The best way is to employ phrases such as: "I can see how you'd be upset," or "I'm sure you're uncomfortable talking about this," or "I know you're uncomfortable with this equipment." It's not hard to be empathetic! It just takes a little time and care.

Let's remember to try to see things through our patient's eyes. And realize that it may be difficult for patients to be honest about how they are experiencing our caregiving.

Vital question #2

How knowledgeable are we about our patient experience scores from the HCAHPS survey or other measuring instruments?

Here is a set of five questions all of us should be able to answer. As an exercise, we ask our seminar attendees to stand while we ask these five questions. If they can answer "yes, they can remain standing. If their answer is "no," they must sit."

1. Do we know your latest patient/resident satisfaction scores that we influence? What are they?

2. Do we know how the scores have changed since the previous report?

3. What are the top two things our patients/residents say that we do best?

4. What are our top two patient/resident dis-satisfiers?

5. Which dis-satisfiers are all of our people working to eliminate?

Out of 100 people guess how many remain standing at the end of question #5? It is usually only a few, if any.

The point must be made – we have to know and understand how these scores inform our service!

AND we have to do something about it!

The answers to these questions give us a much clearer understanding of our patients' experience. The point in keeping up to date on the scores is that...

"Your people can't care about what they don't know about. If they don't know, what is going to change?"

Brian Lee, CSP

Vital question # 3

When a survey asks a patient to rate the skill of a nurse or physician, what do patients really evaluate?

The vast majority of patients don't have the education or background to critically evaluate the technical competence of the staff, but they can evaluate the caregiver's attitude and caring behaviours. Such things as the caregiver's friendliness, thoroughness, ability to explain, listening, etc. We need to consider how our patients may be judging us. Taking a moment to smile and adopt a friendly attitude means a lot to a patient and does not in any way diminish our clinical responsibilities. The patients and family have the ability to evaluate our people skills such as kindness and caring. Their evaluations make up their experience.

Vital question #4

Which does the patient better understand: their clinical treatment or their personal experience?

Does their experience match up with their expectations? We must strive to meet and exceed expectations. So, what are some of the common expectations? What promises were made? A billboard in Southern California read, "Come to St. Bernadine's where we'll treat you like family." Wow, that sounds friendly and caring. It's quite a promise to live up to.

Have you had some of these for yourself or a family member? Having been a patient a few times, these are exactly my expectations.

- I expect to be able to request help within a reasonable amount of time.

- I expect to be kept informed.

- I expect to be listened to.

- I want my questions answered in a way that I can understand.

Let's realize that the patients are going to be asked about their condition by their families, so they're going to have to relate what has been told to them.

What expectations would you add? Would this be a reasonable discussion to have with your staff?

"A patient's last experience is their new expectation."

Ron Tite, Marketing, Branding and Creativity Expert

Vital question #5

When a survey asks a patient to rate your hospital "Overall," or "Willingness to recommend," what do the patients really evaluate?

Is there an overall impression of your facility and the staff? Is the patient satisfied enough to put their reputation on the line with recommendations to others? This requires nothing less than a total buy-in by the entire staff. The patient may experience many positive experiences only to have their overall impression soured by one negative encounter.

For example Patient Mrs. W. was hospitalized for three days. The first two and half days were very positive and filled with friendly caring people and efficient procedures. However, near the end of her stay, she was told that she would be discharged by a certain time. Her family came to pick her up. She waited for four hours beyond the estimated time of discharge. And during that wait, no one ever explained why there was a delay nor was an apology given for the inconvenience. This was enough to negate all of the previous positive experiences and factored into her not giving a high score on the "willingness to recommend" survey question.

This is why it takes a total commitment from everyone at all times to ensure a positive overall impression. It is true that everyone is a caregiver, not just the "hands-on" medical personnel. The ward clerks, admission staff, the housekeepers, transporters, lab and x-ray techs, and people in the business office all have an influence on the patient experience. One IT dept. head referred to his staff as "lifesavers." Indeed, I've felt saved from my antagonistic computer by an IT associate.

Vital question #6

What would be the value if everyone was educated, bought–in, engaged, and empowered as owners and patient advocates?

This requires not only buy-in from the staff but from all leadership.

The value of such a total commitment by everyone cannot be overestimated. It relates to the previous issue of eliminating the "drive-by" and "overall" evaluation of the hospital. This value translates into financial viability, referrals, and repeat business. It also impacts customer loyalty and the reputation of the facility. Remember that your hospital's "reputation" is based on patients' experiences.

Let's not forget the personal impact on the health care providers. A CNA, Ms. T., related that giving herself to her patients and even co-workers constantly bolstered her self-esteem and made her feel worthwhile even in her small duties. Being engaged and empowered affects employee satisfaction.

Renaissance revitalizes the staff and impacts employee satisfaction at all levels, thus reducing costly turnover. After one of our Service Excellence training sessions, a nurse with 12 years of experience stated with teary eyes that she was planning to leave the clinical profession and go into phar-maceutical sales, but that the new spirit of empowerment and dedication to service within the hospital persuaded her to stay in nursing.

Recommendation:

Use these six vital questions to stimulate the thinking and commitment of your staff. Let them be a guide to implementing positive changes in the patient's experience. Before proceeding with any process involving patient satisfaction, make sure you have total buy-in from everyone.

Brian Lee

## CHAPTER 6

What Differentiates You?

What is the one thing that can differentiate you from your competitors?

Answer: The patient's experience with your people.

What are the top factors people weigh when choosing a hospital:

Reputation	28.7%
Personal experience with the hospital	21.1%
MD told me	22.8%
Hospital advanced technology	12.6%
Convenient to home	10.0%

— Health View Plus Survey

Notice that 49% of the factors above directly relate to the patient experience.

When people brag to us about their hospital stay, what do they talk about? It's always their experience with the staff. Here are a few actual real-life comments from patients who've had a positive experience:

- *"I hardly ever have to wait when I go in for my clinic appointment."*

- *"They're always so friendly when I call, even when I call to cancel or have to change an appointment."*

- *"The nurses are all so friendly and check with me often."*

- *"Several doctors and other staff members told me exactly what to expect every step of the way before my procedure."*

- *"They seemed very concerned about controlling my pain."*

- *"Even the transporter guy was a kick."*

- *"I had choices for my meals and even some snacks. The food wasn't like home but was better than I expected."*

- *"I always had enough help getting to and from the bathroom."*

- *"I felt safe and secure the whole time I was there."*

These are the experiential factors which differentiate you from your competitors. Ask yourself: "How hard is it to get the patients to respond positively to their experience?"

We provide these common caring courtesies while we go about our tasks. It takes very little extra effort to enhance the patient experience. And it's why we're there.

Remember, when they don't come back or bad-mouth your facility, you go out of business.

Let's look at some alarming statistics:

FACT: 98 rural hospitals have shut down since 2010. The latest is Mercy hospital in Independence, Kansas.

FACT: 700 rural hospitals across the country are in danger of going under.

– National Rural Health Association 2019

Recommendation:

Hardwire your patient experience initiative as your sustained competitive advantage. Have frequent conversations with the staff about the critical importance of differentiating yourself by providing caring experiences.

Brian Lee

## CHAPTER 7

The Four *"Must-Haves"*

What are the four must-haves we must have to initiate the Renaissance?

What are the four "Must-Haves" to become the hospital that your patients will recommend? What are the essential elements that drive the overall patient experience?

Previously, top hospital leaders thought the following six "Must-Haves," were necessary to improve the patient experience. Would you agree with these? What would you add or take away?

1. New facilities

2. Private rooms

3. Food on demand

4. Bedside interactive computers

5. Unlimited visiting hours

6. More time so patients could rest

— Merlino and Ramar 2013

Our research into this question differs substantially from the above: The following are the "must-haves" that we are convinced drive the overall patient experience.

1. Culture

2. Frontline engagement

3. Leadership engagement

4. Patient engagement

— HCAHPS Breakthrough Leadership Series™

Recommendation:

Analyze each of these four *"must-haves,"* in more detail.

## CHAPTER 8

1st Must-Have:
Culture

Culture:

"The culture of an organization is how people act when no one is watching."

> – *Dr Kevin Joseph*
> *UC Health Univ. of Cincinnati*

Our Culture of Caring

Culture is usually referred to as the arts and other manifestations of human intellectual achievement regarded collectively. It can also be defined as a set of ideas and behaviours of a certain group of people. Hence, we may have a "military culture," an "academic culture," a "capitalist culture," a "service culture," etc. Is there a culture of "exceptional customer service" at your facility? This is what we must strive to achieve.

Another common way to describe culture: it is the way we typically do things around here. There are no written rules. In hospitals, "culture" is explained by the sum total of the patient's experience. We must ask ourselves: Is our culture patient driven or task driven? Ask your frontline people the following: "What words would you use to describe our hospital culture today?"

Here are some choices to consider:

Our hospital is…

  … Patient driven

  … Task driven

  … Job driven

  … Culture driven

  … Financially driven

In 99% of the time, the answer given is, "financially driven" but the reality is "task driven." And this is simple to understand. It's easy for all of us to get caught up with the tasks and responsibilities of our job. We're busy, and we're all under some pressure to "get 'er done." Unfortunately, sometimes the compassionate, caring behaviors may suffer when the focus is on task accomplishment.

"Change your culture or be doomed to repeat the past. You may well ask, How? The answer: The 5 Imperatives of a Patient Driven Culture."

– Brian Lee CSP

The hardest thing to change is the culture. What are the imperatives that comprise culture change?

1. Education

2. Buy-in

3. Engagement

4. Empowerment

5. Ownership and Patient Advocacy

The 5 Imperatives of a
Patient Driven Culture

Retention/Ownership

Owners and Patient Advocates

Empowerment

Engagement

Buy-in

Education

Turnover/Renter-ship

Recommendation:

In order to develop ownership and maintain the culture of extraordinary service, we must systematically implement these five imperatives.

CHAPTER 9

2nd Must-Have: Frontline Engagement

There are five imperatives of frontline engagement.

- Imperative #1 — Education

- Imperative #2 — Buy-In

- Imperative #3 — Staff Engagement

- Imperative #4 — Empowerment

- Imperative #5 — Ownership

"I've learned that people will forget what you said, people will forget what you did, but people will never forget how you made them feel."

– Maya Angelou

If you want your employees to value caring and nurturing your patients, you must value and care for your employees. Press Ganey did a study ten years ago which showed that a 1% improvement in employee morale yields a 2% change in patient satisfaction. Your patient satisfaction scores reflect your employee morale.

CHAPTER 10

IMPERATIVE #1 OF FRONTLINE ENGAGEMENT

Education

Archimedes said, *"Give me a lever long enough and (single-handed) I can move the world."* That lever is education.

Where are your people learning about how to communicate with patients?

At home? In college courses? From friends?—unlikely.

From supervisors?—perhaps, sometimes, hopefully.

But we can do better.

We like to promote a set of behaviours when educating employees. It is called, our "license to please," which is comprised of a five-point empowerment bundle. Much of the following has to do with communication.

1. **The six-foot rule.** At a distance of six feet from another person *(patients, families, vendors, or staff)*, we smile, acknowledge, and greet. Consider the positive experience of being in a facility where this is common. On the other hand, can we appreciate the negative impression when a staff member passes a leader or fellow staff member without any acknowledgement?

2. **The no-pass zone.** This is all about being a patient advocate and engaging in "can-do" behaviours for the patient. Plead their case, get them what they need, do whatever you can, to do what's best for the patient. Anyone who notices a blinking room light can knock, enter the room and offer assistance. You don't have to be a nurse in order to help. Do not pass-by! One hospital reported that one of their elderly patients was impressed that at his hospital, several members of the staff stopped and offered to help another patient find their way.

3. **Managing up** is about building confidence in patients and staff members. This is especially important during "hand-offs" as we transfer a patient from one staff member to another, or when talking about other staff members, or while taking a patient to another department. "I'm taking you to X-ray. It's a great department. You'll be in good hands there." Or "Mr. K., our PA will be coming to see you and review your meds. He's a really competent guy." You can

create positive expectations about peers and departments prior to and during hand-offs. So, by managing-up, you're providing reassurance, building confidence in the patient, and breaking down departmental silos. In a three-day stay at a critical access hospital there may be as many as 60 handoffs. Wouldn't it be great if people practised managing-up during each of those transfers?

4. **Freedom to clean.** This is everyone's responsibility. Many hands doing a little complete the task of cleanliness and organization. You don't have to be a housekeeper to help keep your area organized and clean. You don't have to be a housekeeper to pick up some litter. One of the pharmaceutical reps was very impressed when the hospital CEO he was walking with, stopped to pick up a candy wrapper and throw it into a trash receptacle. When the housekeepers are swamped, what's wrong with pitching in? We're all housekeepers and need to take some pride in our workplace.

5. **License to silence**. This is especially important at night. Let's remember that our patient's perception of quiet at night is based on their own bedrooms at home. We really can't match that. So, we must manage the issue by telling our patients that some sounds at night that can't be helped, are the "sounds of caring." Thus, we reposition some of the nightly noise

as a necessary function of a hospital. We can all remind each other of this patient need. We need to engage everyone to commit to speaking in whispers during quiet times and to fix noisy things.

Which of the above five would you make a #1 priority?

1. The Six-Foot Rule

2. No-Pass Zone

3. Managing up

4. Freedom to Clean

5. License to Silence

How do we accomplish frontline engagement Imperative #1 Education?

Recommendation:

Engage the staff in a three-hour seminar taught by their peers, *(we call them "Service Excellence Advisors – SEAs)* with training, once per year. Typically, they teach the seminars in teams of four. Ongoing training ensures constant renewal of guidelines and procedures to promote service excellence. The SEAs become the vanguard of employee engagement. Collectively they become the "Tipping Point" to change the culture.

CHAPTER 11

IMPERATIVE #2 OF FRONTLINE ENGAGEMENT

Buy-In

We stimulate "buy-in" in a number of ways:

- There are the shared experiences on the job.
- Discussions at group meetings help everyone to be on the same page.
- Shared knowledge from educational opportunities.

All of these are incorporated in the stories we tell.

Here is a story that blew us away: Becky Schwartz at Good Shepherd Hospital was working in pediatrics. A baby was in critical condition with a heart valve problem. The parents were notified that the infant wouldn't make it through the night. The parents were unable to get to the hospital at that time. So after her shift ended at 11:00 PM, Becky stayed on and held the baby in her arms until it passed away at 4:00 AM. She gave the gift of her mindful presence. What higher gift can we ever give? You know such stories. You've lived such stories.

We're all aware that there will be times of sadness and grief in our profession. All we can do is give the gift of our mindful, caring presence.

"If I don't have a story, why should I come back?"
– Fred Lee, speaker and author

"Marketing is no longer about the stuff that you make, but about the stories you tell."
– Seth Godin, author and former dot com business executive

The stories we share are the currency of trust. Stories are the shared experiences that form the culture of our hospital.

As staff becomes a part of those stories they "buy-in."

As people agree to the teamwork protocols necessary to provide exceptional customer service we get "buy-in."

As we share the stories we spread the "buy-in."

Recommendation:

Gather and share stories with everyone at every opportunity which relates to patient satisfaction. Collect these gems and revisit them often. Make them part of your culture. Stories inspire. Stories gently instruct. Stories give us real examples to emulate. Stories produce hope. Have you noticed how well-known and successful religious leaders, public speakers and politicians are great storytellers? We remember stories!

CHAPTER 12

IMPERATIVE #3 OF FRONTLINE ENGAGEMENT

Staff Engagement

One key way we engage people is through "inspiring meetings" we have.

- How effective are your meetings?

- Could they be improved?

Here are some proven meeting guidelines:

1. Begin every meeting with brief round-robin reports from everyone of **good news** since the last meeting. This only takes a few minutes. The news can be personal or work related. This gets the meeting off on a positive note often with some humour.

2. Make sure each meeting **provides as much information as possible** to keep the staff informed. This is a top motivator. In the absence of information, speculation and negative impressions evolve. When the staff feel uninformed, they often assume that the leader does not care about them or doesn't approve or like them.

"In the absence of knowing they fill the void with the negative. The negative attitudes and behaviours may follow which negatively impact the patient experience."
– Pat Summit, Head Coach, U. of Tenn. Lady Volunteers Basketball Team

3. **Appreciate** your colleagues. Elemental Learning Theory indicates, "What gets recognized – gets repeated." Catch them doing something right and acknowledge them. Single out individuals who have excelled in some way. This reinforcement sustains people during stressful times and makes them feel appreciated. Reinforcement guarantees maintaining of excellent behaviour. Everyone needs this! And it's easy to do. Use the staff member's name and be specific about what you're reinforcing.

4. **Celebrate** victories and successes. It's okay to have some fun at meetings. Include goodies and some interesting team activities. One fun example is to have everyone bring in their baby pictures and post them on a board for people to guess who they are. Provide a simple prize for the best guesses.

It's important to highlight any positive developments at your department or facility. A story in a McDonald's TV commercial shows an employee showing his acceptance to a college and how the entire work team celebrates. Glenna Salsbury, an exceptional public speaker and past president of the National Speakers' Association, said that "The best place to work is one where: 1. I'm acknowledged for my efforts, 2. The boss knows my name, and 3. Where there is laughter."

5.   Educate. Set aside 5-10 minutes in every meeting to teach or review some point or aspect of Service Excellence. Use elements from our webinar or any educational elements you've been exposed to, including stories that instruct.

6.   Share your power *(empower your staff).* It is a paradox that as the leader shares their power, responsibility and some decision-making, the more powerful a leader they become. You simply can't do it all on your own. It is a leadership function to discern when an employee has had enough experience, knowledge, and trustworthiness to be empowered. Empowerment is given in gradual steps.

7.   Summarize: In your role as a meeting leader at the end of every meeting, you must summarize what has occurred and what decisions have been made at the meeting. This gives everyone a sense of accomplishment. This is also when responsibilities are assigned. Remember the 3 W's and 1 H. (**W**ho will do **W**hat by **W**hen and **H**ow).

8.   Wrap up every meeting with a **positive takeaway**. In a round-robin fashion, each meeting attendee shares what they will take away and implement from the meeting. What did they like and what could be improved. The meeting leader ends the meeting with positive and motivating remarks to take away, as well as expectations for the future.

If you will engage the staff members at the beginning of the meeting and engage them at the end, have some fun along the way and provide information and guidance, you will have truly successful and meaningful meetings. We have received numerous incredible feedback stories from hospitals which have employed these meeting practices.

Recommendation:

Implement the eight attributes of an engaging, inspiring meeting.

CHAPTER 13

IMPERATIVE #4 OF FRONTLINE ENGAGEMENT

Empowerment

To complete this imperative, I challenge all leaders to issue a "License to Please." This little card says I trust you to make judgments and to own your relationship with your patient.

Recap of the License to Please Empowerment Bundle:

1. The Six-Foot Rule
2. No-Pass Zone
3. Managing up
4. Freedom to Clean
5. License to Silence

Let's add two additional best practice imperatives to the five-point empowerment bundle.

6. **Service Recovery:** Let's be honest, mistakes will be made. Patients will sometimes be inconvenienced or kept waiting. Usually, a sincere blameless apology will be sufficient. But there are times (2-3%) when something more is needed. We like to use the term, "Mess up? Fess up. Dress up". So, we messed up (made a mistake). We admit it (Fess up) and apologize. The "dress up" part is when we give the patient something extra to make up for the mistake, to correct an error or to show compassion. The entire staff is empowered to make the decision to issue a gift certificate or meal voucher for example. We trust our staff with the health and wellbeing of our patients; we ought to trust them to make small "dress up" decisions.

The only requirement is to record the event. It's important to know the circumstances in which vouchers are being given to guide changes we can make and also to know when to replenish the vouchers, gift cards, or other materials.

A few examples: *(remember the impact of stories)*

An elderly woman was left stranded at a hospital with no money or means to get home. The staff saw to it that she got a meal and gave her a voucher to take a taxi cab home.

During a long wait, a small child became impatient and upset. A voucher was given to the family to purchase a colouring book and crayons from the gift shop to keep him occupied.

Mistakes will happen. Service recovery is how we manage them.

7. The other additional imperative is **"The Platinum Rule."** This means that whoever hears a complaint becomes the patient's saint. In other words, all staff members are empowered to take responsibility to fix complaints or hand off the patient to someone who can.

An example: A woman requested to see a hospital Chaplin. A CNA immediately contacted the Chaplin's office and arranged for a Chaplin to see the patient within the hour.

The two imperatives above, round out our empowerment plan. What would it mean if your people understood these imperatives and bought into them? How would these imperatives differentiate your hospital from your competitors? How would these imperatives affect the patient's experience?

Which of the 7 Imperatives would you choose as your #1 priority?

"Dream Big & Work Hard"

"There are people who see in you what you don't see in yourself."
> *– Jean Driscoll, American Wheelchair Racer*

You need to see in your people what they have not seen in themselves i.e. that they are engaged, powerful, talented, compassionate people who have potential they haven't used. You see it in them by the way you communicate with them, educate them and hardwire the best practices. You see it in them by reinforcing their efforts.

Recommendation:

#1   Develop a **Service Recovery** policy with a small committee to:

    A.   Continually spread the word about service recovery.

    B.   Supply vouchers and gift materials around the facility.

    C.   Replenish materials used.

    D.   Keep track of the reasons why vouchers were used.

#2   Spread the word about the "**Platinum Rule**." Discuss it at staff meetings and reward people for using it.

CHAPTER 14

IMPERATIVE #5 OF FRONTLINE ENGAGEMENT

Ownership

"You'll never solve your customer service problems until your frontline is engaged and owns them."
– Brian Lee, CSP

In the book, "Tipping Point," Malcolm Gladwell defines the tipping point as that magical moment when an idea, trend, or social behaviour crosses a threshold, tips and spreads like wildfire.

A positive epidemic begins in your health care facility when the critical few of superior infectors with a disproportionate influence, tip the culture to create a positive patient experience as the norm.

If there truly is ownership, key leadership and trained staff can affect the changes necessary to provide exceptional customer service and patient satisfaction. Everyone owns the patient experience.

For the staff, this is a critical factor in retention and reducing turnover. If a staff member is only "renting space," or "working-to rule," they have no buy-in and no ownership. Indifference and a Laissez Faire attitude cannot be tolerated. There must be engagement.

Recruit and train one out of every 15 frontline super stars (Service Excellence Advisors) to teach an annual HCAHPS based 3-hour workshop to their peers. They teach in teams of four. Everyone in the entire hospital partakes of this training in groups of 20-25. This is an investment that we must make to get everyone engaged.

Instead of having an outside trainer who doesn't know you, or a manager people have heard before and perhaps don't like, select your best and brightest frontline folks and train them to teach the workshop in teams of four. Their ability to influence their peers is phenomenal.

After these teams of four have received the training, have a graduation celebration. Invite their managers and family. Make it a special event. Let the Service Excellence Advisors show what they've learned. You'll be amazed at the energy and excitement generated. One CEO in a hospital in Kansas City told me he was "blown away" by the enthusiasm generated by the SEAs. This is a highlight event that myself and all the trainers look forward to and enjoy.

On occasion, some of these team members are reluctant to speak in public and conduct these training sessions. One such nurse, Mrs. B. was nearly paralyzed with the fear of speaking in public. Her team encouraged her and initially reduced her role in introducing each of the other team members as the seminar began. She was able to do that. After this experience, her self-esteem soared, and she told us it had changed her life. In subsequent workshops, she was able to teach some of the material. Your people don't always appreciate how good and capable they are or what they can grow to be.

"The only thing worse than training your employees and losing them is not training them and keeping them."
– Zig Ziglar

Recommendation:

Recruit and train one out of every 15 frontline super stars (Service Excellence Advisors) to teach an annual HCAHPS based 3-hour patient experience workshop to their peers.

Brian Lee

## CHAPTER 15

3rd Must-Have: Leadership Engagement

"The third most effective leader is one who is followed because of fear.
The second most effective leader is followed because of being loved and admired.
The most effective leader is one who empowers others."
— Lao Tsu, 6th century B.C.

Empowerment must be given judiciously in graduated steps after someone has demonstrated that they are trustworthy, and have had enough training or experience to handle the empowered task.

There is a paradox of leadership: the more the leader shares their power, the more effective they become.

The truth is that no leader makes it alone. They all work with and through others.

The key factor to the success of any organization is the leadership. The battles are won in the general's tent. This is where decisions are made, resources allocated, and plans are developed

What does it take to be a leader today? Hold on...

The leader selects, trains, coaches, makes the best use of resources, rewards, reprimands, refines behaviour, retrains, observes, modifies behaviour, helps people to change, builds collaboration, is supportive, and is accountable for results. That's a load! Leadership is not for everyone. The leader's role is evolutionary. The leader must always be growing, changing and developing. School is never out for the leader.

Some views from the top:

"The new leader is a a facilitator, not an order giver."
> *– John Naisbitt, Megatrends*

"Leadership is an exercise of Influence."
> *– Paul Hersey and Ken Blanchard*
> *Management of Organizational*
> *Behavior: Utilizing Human*
> *Resources*

"An army of deer led by a lion is more to be feared than an army of lions led by a deer."

– Philip II of Macedon - father of Alexander the Great

"A leader is a dealer in hope."

– Napoleon

"School is never out for the leader."

– John F. Kennedy

At a rural hospital in Oklahoma I was doing a focus group with supervisors and leaders about HCAHPS scores and a 63-year-old head housekeeper named Loretta said that she found out that on her med-surg. ward, the patient satisfaction scores were at a dismal 27%. She decided to do something about it. She made a point of visiting each patient three times per day just to "be a friend." She announced to the group that her patient satisfaction scores rose to 67% in a short time. We were impressed when she said "MY scores rose to 67%." That's leadership ownership in action.

In the thirty-five years of delivering these programs, we've discovered that the top two fatal mistakes hospital leaders make when evaluating HCAHPS improvements are:

1. Assuming managers and staff know what to do to create Service Excellence.

2. Assuming the staff want to do it.

The first mistake has to do with education and the second has to do with engagement.

The role of the leader is to:

1. Educate your people to know what to do.
   "You can't hold people accountable for what they don't know"
   - *Kathy Stone, Director Of Rehabilitation Appalachian Regional Healthcare*

   But have we given them the tools to be successful in what they do? We can't order them to care. We can't demand them to be kind. We can't force them to go the extra mile. They have to choose to do so!

2. Engage: *"Inspire them to care."* – *Brian Lee CSP*

The single most profound best practice for leaders to inspire their staff is daily C Suite new patient visits. This best practice is called "Visibility Currency of Trust." Here's how it works: the CEO or designated members of the executive team, personally welcome each new patient on the day they are admitted.

The benefits are extraordinary: The staff witness the commitment of their leader. The clear message is that the priority around here is the patient. *(Another benefit: the patients love it.)* One patient quipped, *"I couldn't believe it. The boss of this place came to visit me and asked if I had any special needs. We discovered we were both into fly fishing. I mean this was the head honcho!"*

Rodney Smith, former CEO at Harrisburg Medical Center in Illinois, enters the new patient's room, welcomes them by name, sits down and often holds their hand. As he leaves, he touches them or shakes their hand and reassures them that they're going to be okay, "We're going to look after you."

To paraphrase Ken Blanchard, "Catch your staff doing something right and reward them for their efforts." Rewarding caring and kindness ensures it will continue. People need that kind of ongoing reinforcement from their leaders.

Leaders are concerned about how to get patients and employees to listen to them. Here are a few suggestions:

1. Hold their attention with eye-contact.

2. Reduce, minimize, or eliminate distractions.

3. Speak clearly and concisely at the appropriate level for this listener.

4. Summarize or paraphrase yourself.

5. Discuss benefits to them *(we persuade with benefits)*.

6. Enrich your message with gestures, facial expressions, examples, illustrations, demonstrations, humour and stories.

In order to influence the staff, the leader must be fully HACHPS competent and be able to field such questions as "What are the current patient satisfaction scores? How are they changing? How can we use these scores and trends to create positive change?" A manager at a rural hospital in Utah said, "I know the scores, but I don't know how to fix them."

School is never out for the leader. Therefore, we recommend you educate your leadership staff by utilizing the HCAHPS Breakthrough Leadership Series™.

This means devoting one hour per month *(for 13 months)* to study the HCAHPS certification program. This is best done in groups rather than individually. To minimize any disruption in services, one very successful method is by having a "lunch and learn" session each month. The training lasts approximately one hour and is best followed by a 30-minute discussion of the topic of the day. There is an HCAHPS certification exam at the end of the series. This year alone we have 300 newly certified leaders who have successfully taken this program.

Consider the value of every leader being HCAHPS competent. This will help ensure that the leaders can explain, discuss, and disseminate important information regarding HCAHPS scores, what they mean and how to best use them as important feedback.

It is free and vital for all clinical and ancillary department leaders.

You can register for the HCAHPS certification program at:

www.webinars.customlearning.com/join/RuralHC

Recommendation:

Educate your leadership staff by utilizing the HCAHPS Breakthrough Leadership Series™.

## CHAPTER 16

4th Must-Have: **Patient Engagement**

Ask your staff what it means to engage patients.

Some of the answers we got from SEAs :

- "Show interest in them."
- "Ask them about themselves, their job, family and past times."
- "Check their name when you come into their room and greet them by name."
- "Listen actively."
- "Smile and demonstrate a positive attitude."
- "Keep them informed as to daily activities and procedures."
- "Ask them if they have questions."

One of the simplest and most effective tools to engage the patient is a short period of chat time. Yes, we can afford the time. And the daily chat time physical tool – the chair.

"When you sit, you are Heart to Heart with the patient."
– Brian Lee, CSP

A revealing study was done evaluating how patients perceived time spent with a nurse. In each case, the nurse spent exactly 5 minutes talking with the patient. In 500 instances, the nurse remained standing and in 500 other cases, the nurse sat. After each event the patients were asked to estimate the amount of time the nurse had spent with them. When the nurse stood, the patients reported that the nurse spent an average of 2-3 minutes talking with them. When the nurse sat, the patients reported that the nurses spent 15 minutes talking with them. Remember, each nurse actually spent 5 minutes with each patient.

Think of how easily you sit when you talk to your children or grandchildren. We know this as relationship building. Nurses tell us that when you build a relationship with a seated chat time at the beginning of the shift – everything goes smoother for the rest of the day. Even mistakes are handled better.

Recommendation:

Implement a very best practice called "Daily chat time from a chair."

CHAPTER 17

Conclusion

Our overall recommendations:

1. Get clear about the numbers. Calculate the "Drive-By" factor.

2. Engage by asking, not telling. Remember the "Six Vital Questions."

3. Only the patient's experience matters as a differentiator.

4. Employ the four "Must Have's."
   - Culture shift
   - Frontline engagement
   - Leadership engagement
   - Patient engagement

"Renaissance starts with You! To be a great leader, you don't have to point the way; you need to blaze a trail."
> *– Mark Cheney, Lab Manager,*
> *Comanche County Medical Center*

"If you're going to act, act with urgency. All change fails because of a lack of urgency."
> *– Professor John Kotter*

Recommendation:

So, the final questions that you need to ask yourself are:

1. What will I do in the next 14 days?

2. What will be my first step?

3. What will be my priority?

Brian Lee CSP
Author & Keynote Speaker

For further information about Brian's availability to keynote your next conference or meeting.

1.800.667.7325 x 200
brian@customlearning.com
www.customlearning.com

"Captivating, directed to Hospital/Clinic needs, and inspiring."

> – Dan David, Director Admission Services, Northern Inyo Hospital, Bishop, CA

"Nailed it."

> – Brian Lady, CEO, Concho County Hospital, Eden, TX

"Very good, met or exceeded expectations."

> – Don Kelso, Education Director Indiana Rural Health Association, Terre Haute, IN

Brian Lee

ADDENDUM A

Recommended Reading List

Anatomy of an Illness by Norman Cousins, Bantam Books, New York, 1979 (A classic)

Crucial Conversations by Patterson,K., Grenny J., McMillan R., Switzler A. McGraw-Hill New York, 2002.

The Carrot Principle by Gostick A. and Elton C. Simon & Schuster New York, 2007.

How Full is Your Bucket? by Tom Rath and Donald O. Clifton Ph.D. Gallup Press, New York, 2004.

"Rural Horizons" Magazine, NRHA Quarterly. For info. – editor@NRHQArural.org

"Journal of Rural Health" Quarterly pub. By NRHA pub. — Blackwell Publishing.

"The Role of Small and Rural Hospitals and Care Systems in Effective Population Health Partnerships." Chicago Il. Health Research and Educational Trust . Accessed at www.hpoe.org, June 2013.

RHIhub (Rural Health Information Hub) On-line library. "Rural Hospitals" Weekly Newsletter 2015.

National Rural Health Resource Center Info. – ruralcenter.org

"Urban and Rural Hospitals. How do They Differ?" James M. Hatten and Rose L. -- Connection Health Care Finance Review. 2017.

Alexander, Brian. **"America's Rural Hospitals are Dangerously Fragile."** The Atlantic, Jan. 9, 2018.

"Small or Rural Update." Am. Hospital Assn. 2017 AHAhelp@aha.org

"Improving Rural Health: State Policy Options." National Conference of State Legislatures, Aug. 2016.

"Solutions for Rural Hospitals. Keep More of Your Patients with High Quality Continuity of Care." Rural Physicians Group, 2018.

"Benefits for Critical Access Hospitals and Other Small Rural Hospitals." HealthIT.gov Aug. 2017.

Roll Call Podcast. **"Opinion: To Renew Rural Health Care, Ditch the One-Size-Fits-all Model."** Senator Bryon L. Dorgan and Kaitlan Krutsick, Wash. DC, April. 2018.

"Four Ways to Reinvent Service Delivery." Harvard Business Review. Ramlis, K. Teisberg, G. and Tucker, A., Dec. 2012.

"The Community Hospital Survival Guide: Strategies to Keep the Door Open." Ayla Ellison, Becker's Hospital Review, June, 2015.

"Original Research at a Small Rural Hospital – You Can Do It." American Nurse Today. J. of American Nurses Assn., Danette Melvin and Maureen Brophy, Oct. 2016, v.11 #10.

Raving Fans, Blanchard, Ken, and Bowles, Sheldon. Wm. Morrow and Co., New York, 1993.

ADDENDUM B

This information is reprinted with permission from the
National Rural Health Association.

About Rural Health Care

The obstacles faced by health care providers and patients in rural areas are vastly different than those in urban areas. Economic factors, cultural and social differences, educational shortcomings, lack of recognition by legislators and the sheer isolation of living in remote areas all conspire to create health care disparities and impede rural Americans in their struggle to lead normal, healthy lives.

Workforce Shortage Problems

- Ease of access to a physician is greater in urban areas. The patient-to- primary care physician ratio in rural areas is only 39.8 physicians per 100,000 people, compared to 53.3 physicians per 100,000 in urban areas. This uneven distribution of physicians has an impact on the health of the population.

- There are 30 generalist dentists per 100,000 residents in urban areas versus 22 per 100,000 in rural areas.

Socioeconomic Factors

- Rural residents tend to be poorer. On average, per capita income in rural areas is $9,242[4] lower than the average per capita income in the United States, and rural Americans are more likely to live below the poverty level. The disparity in incomes is even greater for minorities living in rural areas. About 25 percent of rural children live in poverty.

- People who live in rural America rely more heavily on the Supplemental Nutrition Assistance Program (SNAP) benefits program. According to the Center for Rural Affairs, 14.6 percent of rural households receive SNAP benefits, while 10.9 percent of metropolitan households receive assistance. In all, 1.1 million households receive SNAP benefits.

- Rural residents have greater transportation difficulties reaching health care providers, often traveling great distances to reach a doctor or hospital.

- Tobacco use is a significant problem among rural youth. Rural youths over the age of 12 are more likely to smoke cigarettes (26.6 percent versus 19 percent in large metro areas). They are also far more likely to use smokeless tobacco, with usage rates of 6.7 percent in rural areas and 2.1 percent in metropolitan areas.

- Fifty-three percent of rural Americans lack access to 25 Mbps/3 Mbps of bandwidth, the benchmark for internet speed according to the Federal Communications Commission.[8] Lack of high-speed internet access can be a hindrance to accessing information, representing another challenge rural Americans face.

- Rural communities have more uninsured residents, as well as higher rates of unemployment, leading to less access to care.

Health Inequity

- More than 50 percent of vehicle crash-related fatalities happen in rural areas, even though less than one-third of miles traveled in a vehicle occur there.

- In rural areas there is an additional 22 percent risk of injury-related death.

- Rural areas have more frequent occurrences of diabetes and coronary heart disease than non-rural areas.

- Mental health creates new challenges in rural areas, such as:
    - **Accessibility**: Rural residents often travel long distances to receive services, are less likely to be insured for mental health services, and less likely to recognize the illness.
    - **Availability**: Chronic shortages of mental health professionals exist, as mental health providers are more likely to live in urban centers.
    - **Acceptability**: The stigma of needing or receiving mental health care and fewer choices of trained professionals create barriers to care.

- Rural youth are twice as likely to commit suicide.

National Rural Health Snapshot	Rural	Urban
Percentage of population	19.3%	80.7%
Number of physicians per 10,000 people	13.1	31.2
Number of specialists per 100,000 people	30	263
Population aged 65 and older	18%	12%
Average per capita income	$45,482	$53,657
Non-Hispanic white population	69-82%	45%
Adults who describe health status as fair/poor	19.5%	15.6%
Adolescents who smoke	11%	5%
Male life expectancy in years	76.2	74.1
Female life expectancy	81.3	79.7
Percentage of dual-eligible Medicare beneficiaries	30%	70%
Medicare beneficiaries without drug coverage	43%	27%
Percentage covered by Medicaid	16%	13%

All information in this table is from the Health Resources and Services Administration and Rural Health Information Hub.

Family physicians comprise only 15 percent of the U.S. outpatient physician workforce nationwide, but they provide 42 percent of the care in rural areas.

ADDENDUM C

Rural Hospital Renaissance™
Hospital Assessment Tool

Survival Index

OVERVIEW

Many articles and research discuss factors that determine the survivability of rural hospitals. Most of them are one dimensional and focus on financial, volume, and lagging factors tied to revenue. This Index takes a more pro-active comprehensive view looking at all the leading indicators that ultimately have an impact on your hospital's ability to survive in today's economy.

Step #1 Please rate your perception of your local hospital/ health system's effectiveness using this 5 Star rating scale: 5 = excellent, 4 = very good, 3 = adequate 2 = needs improvement, 1 = needs considerable improvement. If you are not certain about the exact rating, use your intuition or gut feeling.

Step# 2 Add up your star ratings to conclude your total rating, count one point per star.
Example: 3 Star, 4 Star and a 1 Star rating = 8 points.

Step # 3 Insert your total star points in column "B" (below) and in column "C" divide "B" by "# of Criteria" to calculate your average star rating for each Success Factor.

This is a CONFIDENTIAL SURVEY – Not to be duplicated without the expressed written consent of the participating Hospital.

Complete the Survival Index online at
www.savingruralhospitals.com

#	# Of Criteria	**Survival Index** Success Factor	**A** Potential Total Star Points	**B** My/Our Total Star Points	**C** My /Our Average Star Rating *(Divide Column B by #)*
I	23	Provider of Choice/ Patient Experience	115		B ÷ 23
II	14	Employer of Choice / Employee Engagement	70		B ÷ 14
III	5	Physician Engagement	25		B ÷ 5
IV	3	Clinical	15		B ÷ 3
V	5	Growth	25		B ÷ 5
VI	24	Financial	120		B ÷ 24
	74	**TOTAL OVERALL**	**370**		B ÷ 74

I	PROVIDER OF CHOICE / PATIENT EXPERIENCE	
#	**Survival Success Factor** *The Hospital / Health System I am rating:*	Please write the star rating from 1 - 5 Stars
1	**Inpatient (HCAHPS) Patient Experience Star Rating** *Provides a consistent 5 Star patient experience, as reported on Hospital Compare.com, and via its own patient experience survey.*	
2	**Emergency Department (ED CAHPS) Patient Experience Star Rating** *Provides a consistent 5 Star patient experience, as reported via its own patient experience survey.*	
3	**Medical Clinic Scores (CG CAHPS) Patient Experience Star Rating** *Provides a consistent 5 Star patient experience, as reported via its own patient experience survey.*	
4	**Ambulatory Surgery Scores (OAS CAHPS) Patient Experience Star Rating** *Provides a consistent 5 Star patient experience, as reported via its own patient experience survey.*	
5	**Outpatient Patient Experience Star Rating** *Provides a consistent 5 Star patient experience, as reported via its own patient experience survey.*	
6	**Home Health Scores (HH CAHPS) Patient Experience Star Rating** *Provides a consistent 5 Star patient experience, as reported via its own patient experience survey.*	
7	**Long Term Care Scores Resident Experience Star Rating** *Provides a consistent 5 Star patient experience, as reported via its own patient experience survey.*	
8	**Patient Experience Measurement Improvement** *Has coordinated an engaging process to ensure the effective utilization of patient experience measurement surveys and the corresponding leader's, provider's, and frontline staff's literacy of these reports.*	
9	**Social Media Reputation** *Has a positive 5 Star patient experience, as reported on social media such as Google, Facebook, Rate MDS, Yelp etc, and an active process for using this feedback for continuous improvement.*	

I	PROVIDER OF CHOICE / PATIENT EXPERIENCE	
#	**Survival Success Factor** *The Hospital / Health System I am rating:*	Please write the star rating from 1 - 5 Stars
10	**Community Branding** *Has a positive image and reputation in the primary and secondary market it serves.*	
11	**Frontline Patient Experience Education** *Invests a minimum of 3 hours a year educating everyone on skills, best practices, and processes to continuously improve the patient experience, based upon the organizations Mission, Values, and Service Standards.*	
12	**Frontline, Peer Based, Train-the-Trainer Model** *Annually recruits its brightest and best frontline employee to teach patient experience improvement to their peers, as well as coach them on the daily process of continuous improvement.*	
13	**Frontline Engagement and Empowerment** *Has effectively engaged and empowered frontline caregivers to own the relationship with their patients and families.*	
14	**Nursing Patient Experience Education** *Ensures nurses have been educated on a broad range of communication skills that overlap with clinical in such areas as Communication about Medicine, Communication with Nurses, Discharge Information, Pain Care, Responsiveness, and Transition of Care.*	
15	**Emergency Department Process Improvement** *Continuously assesses its throughput processes and caregiver education and engagement, for the purpose of sustaining a 5 Star service level and follows best practice benchmarks for patients time at key bottlenecks within the process of care.*	
16	**Emergency Department Patient Experience Education** *Invests a minimum of 3 hours a year educating Emergency Department caregivers on skills, best practices, and processes to continuously improve the ED patient experience, including topics such as Throughput Management and Collaboration with other depts such as Imaging, Lab, Med Surg, etc.*	

I	PROVIDER OF CHOICE / PATIENT EXPERIENCE	
#	**Survival Success Factor** *The Hospital / Health System I am rating:*	Please write the star rating from 1 - 5 Stars
17	**Medical Clinic Process Improvement** *Continuously assesses and improves its access management, people, paper flow processes, caregiver education, and engagement for the purpose of sustaining a 5 Star service level.*	
18	**Medical Clinic Patient Experience Education** *Invests a minimum of 3 hours a year educating Clinic caregivers on skills, best practices, and processes to continuously improve the patient's experience, including topics such as access management, and Physician/Advanced Care Practitioner communication skills.*	
19	**Inpatient/HCAHPS Improvement Leadership Education** *Has successfully educated leaders at every level on the specific skills and best practices of improving Inpatient/HCAHPS scores.*	
20	**Patient Experience/Service Excellence Council** *Leads the patient experience improvement initiative through an effectively chartered, Patient Experience/Service Excellence Council.*	
21	**Core Best Practices** *Has implemented foundational core best practices such as Huddles, DO ITs, Service Recovery, Service Standards, Key Words/Sentence Starters, etc.*	
22	**Nursing Kindness Culture Best Practices** *Has hardwired key nursing-based best practices such as Nurse Leader Rounding, Purposeful Hourly Rounding, Bedside Reporting, and Post Discharge Calls, etc.*	
23	**Nursing Staff Efficiency** *Through the use of Huddles, Process Improvement meetings or other similar LEAN systems, continuously improves nurse work process to ensure patient safety, communication, reduction of paperwork and compliance.*	
Sub Total	*Add total number of stars for all 23 categories and divide by 23 to calculate your average star rating.*	

II	**EMPLOYER OF CHOICE / EMPLOYEE ENGAGEMENT**	
#	**Survival Success Factor** *The Hospital / Health System I am rating:*	Please write the star rating from 1 - 5 Stars
1	**Employer of Choice Culture** *Is perceived by its employees, leaders and physicians to be a supportive, team-based place to work, and enjoys a reputation for a positive culture on websites such as Indeed and Glassdoor.*	
2	**Employee Engagement Survey** *Measures employee engagement and job satisfaction annually, and uses the feedback to continuously improve, and earn a 5 Star rating from its caregivers.*	
3	**C Suite Currency of Trust** *Has a CEO, C Suite, and Leadership team that are respected, trusted, and skilled at valuing and engaging their frontline and consistently implements key communication best practices such as Quarterly Town Hall Forums and Daily Leadership Huddles.*	
4	**Leadership Communication** *Values the importance of good communication with their caregivers and embraces key best practices such as Daily Staff Rounding, Huddles, and Inspiring Staff Meetings.*	
5	**Leadership Accountability** *Has effectively installed an annual system to hold leaders accountable for their employee retention and morale, and patient experience scores.*	
6	**Leadership Empowerment Skills Education** *Consistently invests at least 2 days a year educating leaders at every level on the skills and best practices of how to motivate and engage their people.*	
7	**Employee Turnover** *Has a stable workforce of engaged staff as measured by Total Annual Turnover.* *1 Star = >35%, 2 Star = 29-35%, 3 Star = 22-28%, 4 Star = 15-21%, 5 Star = <15%*	
8	**Onboarding, Retention, and Recruitment** *Has a systematic process for successfully engaging, onboarding, retaining, and recruiting employees.*	

II	EMPLOYER OF CHOICE / EMPLOYEE ENGAGEMENT	
#	**Survival Success Factor** *The Hospital / Health System I am rating:*	Please write the star rating from 1 - 5 Stars
9	**Human Resources Policy and Performance Appraisal** *Has a progressive set of policies and protocols that attract and retain good people such as Effective Leader Performance Appraisal, Corrective Action Coaching, etc.*	
10	**Awards and Appreciation** *Has an effective ongoing process to acknowledge and appreciate its caregivers for service "above and beyond" for patients and peers.*	
11	**Workforce Availability** *Adequate workforce supply, not requiring any significant use of Agency.*	
12	**Effective Board Leadership** *Has a knowledgeable Board, that understands its role in setting policy and its fiduciary responsibility.*	
13	**IT/Electronic Medical Record Support** *Has an effective EHR system in place and provides its caregivers, providers, and leaders with timely effective IT support.*	
14	**Break Down Interdepartmental Barriers and Silos** *Has created cross-functional teamwork that has broken down needless interdepartmental communication barriers and enhances a seamless patient experience.*	
Sub Total	*Add total number of stars for all 14 categories and divide by 14 to calculate your average star rating.*	

III	PHYSICIAN ENGAGEMENT	
#	**Survival Success Factor** *The Hospital / Health System I am rating:*	Please write the star rating from 1 - 5 Stars
1	**Physician Engagement** *Has successfully educated and engaged Physicians and Advanced Care Practitioners who have bought into the mission of continuously improving the patient experience.*	
2	**Provider Staffing** *Is adequately staffed with sufficient Physicians and Advanced Care Practitioners. Start at 5 and deduct one star for every unfilled vacancy, to a minimum of 1.*	
3	**Provider Productivity Incentives** *Operates its Clinic(s) with employed Physicians and Advanced Care Practitioners, with an incentive-based compensation plan (ie RVUs).*	
4	**Robust Specialist Clinic** *Has a robust diversity of visiting specialist physicians.*	
5	**Physician/ACP Kindness Culture Plan** *Has implemented a set of key best practices to continuously improve the patient experience such as Comparative Ranking of provider patient experience scores and setting an annual threshold goal.*	
Sub Total	*Add total number of stars for all 5 categories and divide by 5 to calculate your average star rating.*	

IV	CLINICAL	
#	**Survival Success Factor** *The Hospital / Health System I am rating:*	Please write the star rating from 1 - 5 Stars
1	**Clinical Excellence** *Delivers excellence in clinical quality and earns a 5 Star rating on CMS Hospital Compare Overall Star Rating or The Joint Commission. One star for each Hospital Compare star awarded.*	

IV	CLINICAL	
#	**Survival Success Factor** *The Hospital / Health System I am rating:*	Please write the star rating from 1 - 5 Stars
2	**Patient Safety** *Has earned a 5 Star or "A" rating for patient safety as reported on LeapFrogGroup.org or HealthGrades.com.* *One star for each grade increment: 1 Star = F, 2 Stars = D, 3 Stars = C, 4 Stars = B, 5 Stars = A*	
3	**Telehealth** *Has a strong telehealth affiliation with a tertiary hospital.*	
Sub Total	*Add total number of stars for all 3 categories and divide by 3 to calculate your average star rating.*	

V	GROWTH	
#	**Survival Success Factor** *The Hospital / Health System I am rating:*	Please write the star rating from 1 - 5 Stars
1	**Market Share** *Is experiencing market share growth in its primary and secondary market areas.*	
2	**Competition** *Has limited nearby competition (ie none within 30 miles).*	
3	**Inpatient Volume Growth** *Has a consistently improving inpatient volume for the past 3 years.*	
4	**Outpatient Volume Growth** *Has a consistently improving outpatient volume for the past 3 years.*	
5	**Emergency Department Volume Growth** *Has a consistently improving emergency volume for the past 3 years.*	
Sub Total	*Add total number of stars for all 5 categories and divide by 5 to calculate your average star rating.*	

VI	FINANCIAL	
#	**Survival Success Factor** *The Hospital / Health System I am rating:*	Please write the star rating from 1 - 5 Stars
1	**Net/Operating Margin** *Has achieved a positive net/operating margin, as noted below.* *1 Star = 1%-10% negative, 2 Star = 1% negative – break even, 3 Star = break even, 4 Star 0% – 2% positive, 5 Star = >2% positive*	
2	**Days Cash on Hand** *Has a positive # days cash on hand as noted:* *1 Star = <50, 2 Star = 51-100, 3 Star = 101-150, 4 Star = 151-200, 5 Star = >200*	
3	**Uncompensated Care** *Has a manageable level of uncompensated care as noted: 1 Star = >5%, 2 Star = 4-5%, 3 Star = 3-4%, 4 Star = 2-3%, 5 Star = <2%*	
4	**Days Patients Accounts Receivable** *Has a positive management of # days of patient accounts receivable, as noted: 1 Star = >75, 2 Star = 65-75, 3 Star = 55-64, 4 Star = 45-54, 5 Star = <45*	
5	**Debt-to-Capitalization Ratio** *Has a manageable debt-to-capitalization ratio.*	
6	**Age of Physical Plant** *Has continuously invested capital in its facilities and concurrently addresses all infrastructure needs.*	
7	**New Technology** *Is able to continuously invest in new technology through purchase or lease.*	
8	**Average Daily Census (ADC)** *Has a stable or growing inpatient census (including swing beds), as noted: 1 Star = <3 ADC, 2 Star = 4-6 ADC, 3 Star = 7-9 ADC, 4 Star = 10-12 ADC, 5 Star = 13+ ADC*	
9	**Tax Support** *Receives significant tax support via a county affiliation, elected tax district, or local sales tax.*	
10	**Critical Access Hospital Cost Report Reimbursement** *Receives meaningful financial benefit from the Critical Access Hospital Cost Report as noted by the Medicare mix: 1 Star = <35%, 2 Star = 35-44%, 3 Star = 45-54%, 4 Star = 55-65%, 5 Star = >65%*	

VI	FINANCIAL	
#	**Survival Success Factor** *The Hospital / Health System I am rating:*	Please write the star rating from 1 - 5 Stars
11	**Upper Payment Limit** *Is located in a state that permits rural hospitals to benefit from the Upper Payment Limit affiliation with skilled nursing homes. 1 Star – no, 5 Star – yes*	
12	**Long-Term Care** *We operate a long-term care/skilled nursing facility that has a negative/positive impact on our net margin. 1 Star = negative financial impact, 5 Star = positive financial impact*	
13	**System Affiliation** *Realizes significant financial stability and benefits due to its affiliation with a hospital system. 1 Star – no, 5 Star – yes*	
14	**Fundraising Foundation** *Has a strong, active fundraising foundation that raises significant capital for plant and equipment on an ongoing basis. 1 Star = no foundation, 2 Star = not effective foundation, 3 Star = helpful foundation, 4 Star = very effective foundation, 5 Star = outstanding foundation*	
15	**Rural Health Clinic Status** *Has one or more medical practices certified as a Rural Health Clinic. 1 Star – no, 5 Star - yes*	
16	**340B Drug Program** *Has been approved for the 340B Drug Program rebate. 1 Star – no, 5 Star – yes*	
17	**Medicaid Expansion** *Is located in a state that has enrolled in Medicaid Expansion. 1 Star – no, 5 Star – yes*	
18	**Healthy Payor Mix** *Has a healthy payor mix, including a significant number of commercially insured patients with private policies. 1 Star = poor payor mix, 5 Star = strong payor mix*	
19	**Population Growth** *Primary and secondary market area has a stable or growing population. 1 Star = declining, 2 Star = stable, 3 Star = 0% - .4%, 4 Star = .5% - 1%, 5 Star = > 1%*	

VI	FINANCIAL	
#	**Survival Success Factor** *The Hospital / Health System I am rating:*	Please write the star rating from 1 - 5 Stars
20	**Unemployment Rate** *Has a stable or declining unemployment rate, compared to the state average* *1 Star = high unemployment, 5 Star = low unemployment*	
21	**Per capita Income** *Operates in a county(s) with a stable or growing per capita income. 1 Star = low per capita income, 5 Star = high per capita income*	
22	**Has an OB Unit** *Has an OB unit with an annual delivery volume.* *1 Star = 10-20, 2 Star = 21-30, 3 Star = 31-40,* *4 Star = 41-50, 5 Star = > 50*	
23	**Financial Management** *Has competent, stable, experienced financial management staff. 1 Star = ineffective, 5 Star = effective*	
24	**Effective Cost Control** *Has a comprehensive tracking system by service line to accurately capture, track and manage costs. 1 Star = ineffective, 5 Star = effective*	
Sub Total	*Add total number of stars for all 24 categories and divide by 24 to calculate your average star rating.*	

This information is reprinted with permission from Stratis Health. It has been excerpted for length. The full report, including detailed methodology, the list of participating hospitals, additional strategies, and resource links can be found at:

www.ruralcenter.org/resource-library/study-of-hcahps-best-practices-in-high-performing-cahs

StratisHealth

RURAL QUALITY
IMPROVEMENT
TECHNICAL ASSISTANCE

A Study of HCAHPS Best Practices in High Performing Critical Access Hospitals

Overview

This resource shares HCAHPS best practices of high performing critical access hospitals (CAHs) identified through focus group discussions with 38 hospitals from across 17 states. The report includes:

- An overview of the HCAHPS survey
- Methodology for selection of high-performing CAHs and the focus group process
- Best practices summarized by HCAHPS topic

Key strategies for each HCAHPS topic reflect the best practices cited most frequently by focus group participants.

Background

The Hospital Consumer Assessment of Health care Providers and Systems (HCAHPS) is a survey instrument developed by the Agency for Health care Research and Quality (AHRQ) in 2002 to measure hospital patient perceptions of care1. The survey has been required by the Centers for Medicare & Medicaid Services (CMS) for all Prospective Payment System (PPS) hospitals since 2007, and results have been publicly reported on Hospital Compare since 2008.

The HCAHPS survey has 32 questions. There are 25 questions divided into 11 topics that track and compare performance (the other seven questions relate to demographics and patient information). Of the 11 topics, seven are composites of two or three questions, including nurse communication, doctor communication, responsiveness of hospital staff, pain management, communication about medicines, discharge information, and care transition. Two of the topics are individual questions related to cleanliness and quietness of the hospital environment, and two of the topics are global questions related to overall rating of the hospital and willingness to recommend the hospital.

HCAHPS participation is currently not required by CMS for the 1,340 critical access hospitals (CAHs) in the United States. However, 1,029 CAHs reported HCAHPS data for the Q1 – Q4 2015 reporting period (the time period used for this study).

One barrier for the utility of HCAHPS for some CAHs is low patient volumes. The HCAHPS survey focuses on inpatient care and many CAHs have limited inpatient census. The survey process also excludes patients that are discharged to hospice, skilled nursing, or nursing home care which further reduces the number of patients who are surveyed each quarter. For hospitals that have at least 100 completed HCAHPs surveys in the most recent four quarters, CMS calculates and publishes an HCAHPS star rating composite on a five point scale, with 5 Stars as the highest rating, and 1 Star as the lowest.

Method – Hospital Selection

Hospital selection for the study was based on achievement of a CMS star rating of 5 Stars, however, hospitals with less than 100 completed surveys in one year are not assigned a star rating. An estimated association between the performance of CAHs with over 100 completed surveys that achieved a CMS 5 Star rating and the performance of CAHs with less than 100 completed surveys was calculated utilizing the average of 11 topic-specific HCAHPS measures. CAHs with an average score greater than 77 percent were included in the selection process.

In aggregate, hospitals participating in the HCAHPS Best Practices Focus Groups performed above the national average in every HCAHPS topic.

HCAHPS Topic or Composite	Focus Group Average	National Average
Response Rate	38%	29%
Overall Rating of Hospital	82%	72%
Willingness to Recommend this Hospital	81%	72%
Communication with Nurses	88%	80%
Communication with Doctors	88%	82%
Responsiveness of Hospital Staff	82%	69%

HCAHPS Topic or Composite	Focus Group Average	National Average
Pain Management	88%	71%
Communication about Medicines	72%	65%
Cleanliness of Hospital Environment	84%	74%
Quietness of Hospital Environment	72%	63%
Discharge Information	89%	87%
Care Transition	61%	52%

Focus Group Findings

HCAHPS Response Rates

HCAHPS surveys can be administered in four ways, or modes: mail only, telephone only, mixed (mail followed by telephone), and interactive voice response (IVR). Studies have indicated that the highest HCAHPS response rates are generated with mixed mode, followed by mail only and telephone only. The national HCAHPS response rate average is 29 percent. Survey response rates of the participating hospitals varied from 18 to 76 percent. Most of the participating hospitals administer mailed surveys only (68%), followed by telephone only (18%), with no appreciable differences between the lower volume and higher volume hospital groups. These numbers are not far from a representation of national mode data, which reflects 60 percent mailed surveys and 40 percent telephone surveys. The average response rate for the focus group hospitals is 38 percent, with a median of 37 percent.

The HCAHPS Quality Assurance Guidelines provide guidance as to what hospitals can and cannot do to prevent bias when they are notifying patients of the HCAHPS survey and it is important that hospitals be familiar with them, especially when using any forms of scripting that might sway patient responses or incentives to complete surveys. Participants of the HCAHPS focus groups described interventions employed to enhance response rates. The most common intervention was to simply notify patients to expect the survey. This was most often done verbally at the time of discharge.

Another frequently described intervention is to ask patients about their satisfaction with their hospital stay during some type of patient rounding, such as leader rounds, discharge planning rounds, or interdisciplinary team (IDT) rounding and remind patients to complete and return the survey, assuring patients that the information would be acted on to improve hospital care. Ten of the participants follow up by reminding patients to complete the survey during discharge phone calls.

Improving Response Rate Strategies:
- Tell patients about the survey
  - Often at discharge
  - Flyer or brochure
  - Posters, hospital website, announcements on waiting room television screens
- Remind patients during discharge phone calls
- Leader rounding – assess patient satisfaction during stay and/or remind of survey
- Weekly or biweekly patient lists to vendors

Overall HCAHPS Success

Focus group participants were asked "What are the one or two most important practices or behaviors you think drive your overall HCAHPS success?" in order to capture interventions likely to influence patient perceptions of overall hospital ratings and willingness to recommend the hospital to others. The top three responses involved practices specifically related to 1) behavior of hospital leaders, 2) HCAHPS data awareness, and 3) intentional efforts to improve the culture of the hospital. Staff engagement followed, at times with a rather blurred margin when differentiating between culture and staff engagement. For example, the term "ownership" was categorized in the context of culture, but is also related to staff engagement.

Participants from hospitals with lower volumes were more likely to attribute HCAHPS success to their "small town, family atmosphere" (9:1), without being able to readily articulate global HCAHPS improvement practices. The lower volume CAHs do score a little higher on overall rating than the higher volume CAHs at 83 percent compared to 81 percent, while the national average overall hospital rating is 72 percent.

Some practices described in response to this global question were also a common response to a specific HCAHPS question or composite. For example, hourly rounding was mentioned five times as a driver of overall HCAHPS success, but was the most frequent response during the discussion on responsiveness of hospital staff and is included in that section of this document.

Culture

Culture is defined as the norms, attitudes and beliefs held among a group of people. Exactly half of the focus group participants attributed their hospital's HCAHPS success to the culture of the organization, using words such as "embedded" or "unified" and "pride" to indicate an intentional and global expectation for positive attitudes and behavior toward patients and toward each other. Phrases to capture the cultural expectations, such as "This matters to us" or "Everything in our power" were adopted by several of the participating hospitals to serve as a true north, or guiding behavioral principle.

Leadership Practices

It is well established that leaders shape the culture of an organization, and focus group participants confirmed this notion with 58 percent of participants attributing their HCAHPS success to leadership behaviors. Several narrowed focus specifically to behaviors of the CEO. Tangible culture shaping leader behaviors were offered, including leader rounding with staff and patients, leadership development opportunities, and CEO visibility and engagement.

Leader rounding with staff can take many forms, but the key concept is an intentional, predictable and ongoing connection of leaders at all levels with providers, staff or supervisors to establish relationships, affirm good work, allow an opportunity for requests, suggestions and concerns to be shared, and to harvest opportunities to recognize and reward employees. Specific quality topics such as HCAHPS may be included in these conversations. Some participating hospital leaders accomplish leader rounding through administrative huddles on units, some through individual meetings with staff and providers, and others with regularly scheduled walk-rounds. Leader rounding in some of the hospitals is incorporated into evaluations to promote consistency. Participants often connected leader rounding with staff satisfaction.

CEO visibility was also described as an important leadership behavior by several of the focus group participants. This visibility involved being on patient care units often, at all hours, talking to staff, patients, families. One such CEO presented the hospital's behavioral standards to new employees, stamping a note of authority and expectation to the standards.

HCAHPS Data Feedback

Over half of the participants across both the higher volume and lower volume groups of CAHs emphasized the importance of sharing HCAHPS data with staff and providers often and in many ways. Data feedback was also brought up as a near-top improvement strategy for almost every HCAHPS question or composite, a confirmation to the crucial nature of scorekeeping in building momentum around performance improvement efforts. Sharing the data and talking about it generates enthusiasm around improvement and lets staff and providers know that leaders are paying attention to progress and that it is important

Staff Engagement

"Happy staff make happy patients" is the prevailing message when it comes to staff engagement as a driver of HCAHPS success. Based on focus group comments, it appears that although staff appreciate celebrations of performance improvement progress, rewards and recognition, a more important component of staff engagement and satisfaction cited by almost 40 percent of participants, is to be consistently and intentionally included in decision making, action planning and problem solving for their departments.

Asking staff to solve problems or improve care and removing barriers to implementation of their ideas is perceived as evidence of being valued. This strategy is a double win in that participants indicated it often creates more effective solutions than when the people closest to the problem are not consulted. HCAHPS results tied to evaluations and compensation, however, were described as drivers of success in several of the lower volume CAHs.

**Overall HCAHPS Success
Key Strategies**

- Culture
    - Standards of behavior
    - Teamwork
    - Accountability
- Leadership practices
    - Leader visibility
    - Leadership development
    - Leader rounding with staff
- HCAHPS Data Feedback
    - Share the data with staff and providers often
    - Provide opportunities for discussion and suggestions
    - Foster friendly competition
- Staff Engagement
    - Consistent, intentional involvement in decision making and problem solving
    - Celebrations of performance improvement progress, rewards and recognition

Additional Strategies
- ▓ Evaluations or pay for performance tied to HCAHPs
- ▓ Hire for fit
- ▓ Dedicated staff or committee
- ▓ Staffing ratios

. . . .

Communication with Nurses

Patient whiteboards are the most frequently cited impactful intervention related to nursing communication, followed by nurse bedside shift report, hourly rounding (discussed under "responsiveness of hospital staff"), scripting, and daily huddles. Other interventions not already addressed during overall HCAHPS performance are nurses rounding with physicians, multidisciplinary rounding, and mandatory scrub colors.

Patient Whiteboards

Patient whiteboards, a tool utilized primarily by nurses to share information with patients and other members of the health care team, are thought to improve nursing communication in nearly three quarters of the participating critical access hospitals. Information included on whiteboards varies from hospital to hospital, but typically includes names of the nurse and physician on duty, treatment goals, activity restrictions, and diet. More detailed versions might add time a patient's next pain medication is due, possible discharge date, services needed at home, and a place for patients to write questions for the health care team.

Nurse Bedside Shift Report

In AHRQ's Guide to Patient and Family Engagement in Hospital Quality and Safety, nurse bedside shift report is included as a key strategy to "help ensure the safe handoff of care between nurses by involving the patient and family". This strategy is also described as a driver of nursing communication success in well over half of the HCAHPS focus group hospitals, overcoming varying degrees of initial resistance to transform the longstanding tradition of a more informal nurse to nurse shift report. In one hospital, the successful change was suggested and initiated by natural nurse leaders, reinforcing the effectiveness of staff engagement and empowerment. That hospital indicated nursing communication HCAHPS score improvements within one quarter.

Scripting

Five of the participating CAHs referenced types of scripting in relation to nursing communication, but the concept came up as an overall HCAHPS driver of success as well as in response to other HCAHPS composites and questions. Scripting provides structure to help nurses and other hospital personnel to communicate effectively and consistently with patients.

Daily Huddles

Daily huddles are another HCAHPS strategy that came up as an overall HCAHPS success strategy as well as in more than one topic of the HCAHPS survey discussion. Huddles typically take place at the same time every day on patient care units, aka, "the floor", and involve multiple disciplines, such as a charge nurse, staff nurses and/or a utilization review nurse, social services, physician, pharmacist, infection preventionist, physical therapist and others. They might also be called daily briefings or multidisciplinary meetings, and vary in terms of structure. A patient by patient approach might be taken to talk about safety concerns, a 24 hour look-back to talk about any patient incidents or situations and how care might be improved, or a conversation that includes present patient census, patient safety issues, and staffing. Patient satisfaction might be woven into the structure of the daily huddles, and in some hospitals, the huddles are immediately followed by patient rounds involving two or more disciplines, such as nursing and pharmacy. Whatever the structure, huddles allow staff an opportunity to verbalize safety concerns and suggest remedies, and foster heightened staff engagement and ownership of patient safety issues.

Communication with Nurses
Key Strategies

- Patient whiteboards
- Nurse bedside shift report
- Data feedback and discussion
- Scripting
- Daily Huddles

Additional Strategies
- Hourly rounding
- Leader rounding with patients
- Nurse engagement/ownership
- Mandatory scrub colors

Communication with Physicians

Not all of the participating HCAHPS Focus Group CAH representatives were able to differentiate between nursing and physician communication practices. Many of the strategies mentioned are echoed nursing communication practices, such as patient whiteboards and daily huddles. The most common driver associated with HCAHPS physician communication success is frequent data feedback on the measure and the friendly competition that ensues between providers and between physicians and nurses.

A practice that came up in both nursing and physician communication, but more frequently related to physician communication, is that of nurses accompanying physicians on rounds, which supports the consistent messaging idea described in daily huddles. Several hospitals provide chairs or stools in patient rooms to encourage physicians to sit down during patient rounds and convey a less rushed and more attentive feel to physician communication. Note pads and pens at the patient bedside provide a consistent place for patients to write questions down between physician visits for review during rounds. Enhanced hospital/physician rapport, an engaged and energetic CMO, and increased physician accessibility associated with hospitalist programs are other attributes associated with physician communication.

· ·

Communication with Physicians Strategies

- Data feedback, friendly competition
- Nurses accompany physicians on rounds
- Sit down during patient visits
- Note pads and pens at bedside for patient questions
- Engaged physician leaders
- Hospitalist programs

· ·

Responsiveness of Hospital Staff

Responsiveness of hospital staff essentially captures how satisfied patients are with the amount of time it takes hospital staff to respond to requests for help.

Hourly rounding is by far the most common practice offered as an important driver of patient satisfaction related to hospital staff responsiveness in both lower and higher volume critical access hospitals. Second is standard that everyone wearing a hospital badge is responsible to answer call lights or patient alarms, often referred to as the "no pass zone." Use of technological devices is third, particularly identified in higher volume CAHs. Other practices tied to hospital staff responsiveness are staff engagement, escorting patients, family members, and visitors to their destinations rather than verbally directing them, consistently asking patients if there is anything else they need before leaving the room, and increasing the presence of certified nursing assistants (CNAs) or patient care technicians (PCTs).

Hourly Rounding

Hourly rounding refers to purposeful patient visits conducted by licensed or unlicensed nursing staff to check on the status of patients and take care of personal needs, in effect, before the patient has to push a call light. Almost 65 percent of the participating critical access hospitals attribute hourly rounding to patient satisfaction related to responsiveness of hospital staff. Several participants add that hourly rounding ultimately contributes to staff satisfaction as well due to a subsequent decrease in patient call light use by patients. The most frequently described hourly rounding model involves licensed nurses alternating with CNAs or PCTs, which helps alleviate nursing resource burden, and several participants stated that rounding is decreased to every two hours during the night shift. Hourly rounds are often structured around what is commonly known as the "4 P's – pain, potty, position, and personal effects or possessions", and usually end with staff asking patients "Is there anything I can get you before I go?" Documentation of hourly rounds may be accomplished using EHR templates, on paper forms posted on patient room doors, or on patient whiteboards.

No Pass Zone

No Pass Zone is a concept that originated with the Hospital Quality Institute where all hospital employees are expected to stop and respond to call lights and patient alarms rather than to pass by. Almost half of the focus group participants indicate that similar expectations are promoted in their hospitals to improve HCAHPS performance related to responsiveness, although not all of them used the "No Pass Zone" terminology. In one hospital the expectation is known as "Everyone's a Caregiver". Patient care requests for non-clinical support such as a beverage or tissue are taken care of immediately by any employee, including the CEO, while requests of a clinical nature are handed off to nursing personnel.

Technological Devices

Technological devices thought to improve response times by hospital staff involve call light system characteristics and nursing communication devices, some of which were connected. Call light systems described include those allowing a patient to specify whether a nurse or CNA is being requested, or to specify the reason the call light is being activated, such as for a beverage, toileting assistance, or a medication. Bed alarms can be integrated into call light systems, flashing different colors outside the room and sounding different alarms. Other systems trigger an alarm at a desk manned by a secretary or a CNA and requests can be forwarded to nursing staff using a portable phone. Two way speakers are installed in patient bathrooms so patients can be reminded not to get up alone, but to wait for someone to help. Some call light systems also accommodate response timeliness auditing.

· ·

Responsiveness of Hospital Staff Key Strategies
- ▓ Culture
  - – Standards of behavior
- ▓ Hourly Rounding
  - – May alternate RNs with CNAs
  - – Four Ps (pain, potty, position, and personal effects)
  - – Documented
- ▓ No Pass Zone
  - – Everyone answers call lights
  - – Non-clinical support can be provided by anyone
- ▓ Technological devices
  - – Call light systems
  - – Two way speakers
  - – Nurse communication devices

Additional Strategies
- ▓ Staff engagement
- ▓ Escorting patients, family members, and visitors
- ▓ Scripting: "Can I get you anything before I go?"

- Certified nursing assistants (CNAs) or patient care technicians (PCTs)
- Patient centeredness and customer service staff education

. . . .

Pain Management

Amidst the complexity of pain medication prescribing during an ongoing opioid abuse epidemic, patients are given an opportunity to evaluate how well hospitals do in managing their pain on HCAHPS surveys. Several of the participants admitted that pain management is a difficult topic due to opioid abuse.

NOTE: In November 2018, CMS announced that it will remove the three Communication about Pain questions from the HCAHPS patient experience survey starting with October 2019 discharges. Although it will no longer be measured through the HCAHPS survey, communication about pain and pain management continues to be a critical component of patient experience.

Patient Whiteboards

Half of the focus group participants state that using white boards to help caregivers to remember to talk about and address pain, and to remind patients what is being done about their pain is a winning strategy in boosting patient satisfaction regarding pain management. There is some variation between hospitals as to exactly what is documented on the boards, but the general principle is the same. Pain scales, pain goals, time of "last given" or "next due" medication dose, and medication and alternative treatments prescribed are some of the pain-related points included on patient white boards.

Setting Expectations and Goals

Another common strategy identified as a driver of patient satisfaction regarding pain management is that of expectation setting. Patient education is provided by a physician or nurse, and at times in a prehospital setting for scheduled hospitalizations, regarding the type of and severity of pain patients might expect in relation to the hospitalization procedure or event, and available treatment options. Clarification that "pain management is not always pain free" helps prepare patients for some pain, and reduce dissatisfaction.

Alternative Therapies

Alternative pain therapies are more frequently related as drivers of pain satisfaction regarding pain in lower volume critical access hospital focus groups. Therapies suggested include those involving heat or cold such as warm compresses, towels, blankets, and ice packs, as well as positioning, relaxing music, aroma therapy, distraction activities, pet therapy and back rubs or massage. One hospital provides a comfort menu with several alternative therapy options for patients to choose from.

Automated Pain Reassessment Reminders

Electronic reminders to check on patients for effectiveness of pain treatments are available in some call light systems and in versions of electronic health record (EHR) systems. In one hospital, a button can be pushed outside of a patient room that sets an alarm in one hour to remind nurses to go back and check on the patient. Most of the automated reminders described, however, are built into the EHR system.

In one system, an initial pain scale value has to be entered and the administering nurse's badge scanned when pain medications are scanned for administration. Fifty minutes after the medication is given, an alarm reminds the nurse to reassess the patient, enter a follow up pain scale value and rescan his or her badge.

Pain Management Key Strategies
- Patient whiteboards
- Setting goals and expectations
- Alternative therapies
- Automated pain assessment reminders

Additional Strategies
- EHR or call system reminders
- Pain management as a nursing quality improvement priority
- Frequent pain assessments
- Hourly rounding
- IV insertion skill development
- Locally administered pain medication during surgery
- Ten minute turnaround time for pain medications

Communication about Medications

Focus group participants most commonly attribute success in this dimension to patient education provided by a pharmacist, closely followed by variations of written patient education on medications. Discharge phone calls, in some hospitals conducted by a pharmacist, medication reconciliation, and using key words such as "education on your medications" and "side effects of your medications" are other practices that are thought to drive HCAHPS communication about medication scores. One hospital offers medication organizers to patients when they are discharged.

Pharmacist Visits

Not surprisingly, the majority of the focus group CAHs with patient education being provided by pharmacists are from the higher volume hospital group. Different approaches to pharmacist visits are taken. Some pharmacists visit every patient at least one time while they are hospitalized to essentially conduct a medication reconciliation review on all of the patient's medications, while others round on all patients every day to talk about any new medications and answer questions. Some pharmacists visit patients to provide education only when new medications are ordered and may return to review all medications on discharge, and some routinely visit all patients at the time of discharge.

Patient Education

Providing patient education is identified as an important practice related to HCAHPS medication communication scores by over half of the focus group participants, with several important details. Most of the time written information is provided on new medications and reviewed right before the new medication is given for the first time, so that patients can hear and read about it before they take it. Medication handouts typically include at the very least, what the medication is for and common side effects. In some of the participating CAHs, EHR hard stops are in place that do not allow further documentation after a new medication is scanned until patient handouts are printed and the nurse documents that patient education is completed. Several participants specified that patient education on medications provided at their hospital is easy to read, common language, very simple, or written at a second grade level, and the Teach-Back method for providing patient education in conjunction with written materials was specified by three participants.

Communication about Medications Key Strategies
- Culture
  - Standards of behavior
- Pharmacist Visits
- Patient Education
  - Easy to read
  - Teach back
- Key Words

Additional Strategies
- Discharge phone calls
- Medication reconciliation
- Bar code scanning
- Medication organizers

Cleanliness of Hospital Environment

There was not as much synergy around any particular interventions for this HCAHPS topic, and many of the focus group comments were directed at the merits of the environmental services department. Two common ideas involved room cleanliness auditing or rounds with varying degrees of formality, and notes on cards or whiteboards drawing patient and family attention to cleaning services performed before or during their hospital stay.

Several of the hospitals established clear expectations that everyone is responsible for environmental cleanliness, and five participants described patient room cleaning schedules that include a thorough cleaning in the morning and a brief evening check in to empty trash cans and "tidy up", which may be performed by a nurse, a CNA, a volunteer or environmental services staff.

Notices of Cleaning Services

HCAHPS is about patient perception, and around half of the focus group hospital participants describe efforts to heighten patient and family awareness to the cleaning that is being done in their rooms before and during their stay. Tent cards are left in newly prepared rooms, whiteboard notes written by environmental services staff, and calling cards are left on bedside tables. Names of staff, the date and time of cleaning and a way to contact environmental services might be included. In one hospital, a creative touch is added by leaving a card tucked in a towel animal on the patient's bedside table.

- -

Cleanliness of Hospital Environment Key Strategies
- ▨ Cleanliness auditing
- ▨ Notices of cleaning services
- ▨ Cleaning schedules

Additional Strategies
- ▨ Everyone is responsible for cleanliness

- Environmental services staff engagement as an integral part of the health care team
- Environmental services staff education on cleaning
- Environmental services staff education on customer service
- Access to environmental services staff via two-way radios or electronic requests
- Patient and Family Advisory Council (PFAC) environmental assessments

. . . .

Quietness of Hospital Environment

The need for rest in order to heal is a paradoxical idea given the bustling activity found in most hospitals. The HCAHPS question on quietness of the hospital environment challenges hospital leaders to find solutions to relieve that paradoxical tension, and many of the critical access hospitals participating in the focus groups have risen admiringly to the challenge. However, among focus group participants, lower volume CAHs do a little better on this measure at 73 percent compared to 71 percent in the CAHs with higher patient volumes. Heightened awareness through ongoing and frequent reminders was most regularly cited as a strategy. Staff reminders are provided in meetings, newsletters, e-mails, and in real time when voices are carrying or groups of people are congregating in hallways near patient rooms. Technological devices utilized to monitor and draw staff attention to noise levels have been used in seven of the focus group hospitals with mixed results. Most participants agreed that the usefulness of these devices is, at best, short term to heighten awareness to noise levels.

Quietness of Hospital Environment Strategies
- Awareness/Reminders
- Structural Changes
- Environmental Noise Control

Additional Strategies
- Quiet times
- Keep patient doors closed
- White noise
- Soothing music on care channels
- Earplugs or pillows

Discharge Information

Generally, hospitals receive fairly high patient ratings on the HCAHPS topic of discharge information. The composite is based on two survey instrument questions with yes or no responses, rather than the "top box" scoring method utilized for other topics:

- "During this hospital stay, did doctors, nurses or other hospital staff talk with you about whether you would have the help you needed when you left the hospital?"

- "During this hospital stay, did you get information in writing about what symptoms or health problems to look out for after you left the hospital?"

Discharge Planning

During the HCAHPS focus group discussions on discharge information, the point was made several times that successful discharge planning for each patient must start at the time of admission. This is accomplished in a variety of ways in the participating hospitals. Discharge planning may be led by a social worker, discharge planning nurse, case manager, or a combination of all three, often in conjunction with a charge nurse and physician.

Discharge Education

Around half of the participating CAH representatives point to some type of discharge education as a strong driver of high HCAHPS survey discharge information scores. Most commonly, a discharge packet, folder, or binder is given to patients early in the admission. One hospital realized a dramatic increase in HCAHPS scores after beginning to give patients one inch binders with separator tabs for different types of education, such as diagnosis, medications, treatments, equipment, and after care. The front cover has a reminder to bring the binder to all follow up appointments.

Contents of discharge packets, binders, or folders are often reviewed at discharge along with written discharge instructions, a discharge care plan, or an after visit summary (AVS), which are typically generated from the EHR. Some participants specified that discharge educators utilize the Teach-Back method for delivering exit care instructions, that all written discharge information is designed to be easy to read, and that plenty of time is allowed for discharge education to help ensure that patients understand what they are being taught.

Discharge Phone Calls or Home Visits

Post discharge follow up, whether by phone or in person, is the most frequently referenced strategy connected to HCAHPS discharge information success. Strategies for implementation vary widely. Discharge phone calls might be conducted by a utilization review nurse, discharge coordinator or planner, or pharmacist, most often two to three days after discharge. Patients are asked about their pain, if they have questions about their medications, and discharge information might be reviewed.

· ·

Discharge Information Key Strategies
- Discharge Planning
- Discharge Education
- Discharge Phone Calls or Home Visits

Additional Strategies
- Whiteboard in nursing care room with names of all patients, discharge plans
- Dedicated staff
- Staff education on discharge planning
- EHR triggers for discharge visits

· ·

Care Transitions

As mentioned earlier, HCAHPS care transitions scores for all hospitals are much lower than HCAHPS discharge information scores, and this disparity also holds true for the focus group CAHs. Transitions of care is a composite of three four-point Likert-type scale questions on the HCAHPS survey:

- "During this hospital stay, staff took my preferences and those of my family or caregiver into account in deciding what my health care needs would be when I left."

- "When I left the hospital, I had a good understanding of the things I was responsible for in managing my health."

- "When I left the hospital, I clearly understood the purpose for taking each of my medications".

A review of the HCAHPS survey questions can help clarify the difference in hospital performance between Care Transitions and Discharge Information, but also reveals a disconnect between the composite name – Care Transitions - and the content of the questions it represents. Although the questions address patient perception and understanding of care needs when they leave the hospital, the majority of the focus group responses in this topic are better aligned with processes for effective transitions of care with strategies such as community care collaboration meetings, readmission committees, and formal care transition programs. Medication reconciliation was offered several times as a strategy, however, and "giving patients control of their care", and "explaining patient responsibilities" also was mentioned. Addressing expectations in patient materials can also be a strategy, for example, first page of a discharge folder given to patients in one hospital states "Discharge planning starts with admission. We want to have a good understanding of your preferences related to discharge needs".

....

Care Transitions Strategies
(not including duplicate discharge Information strategies)

- Community care collaboration
- Readmission committee
- Care transition programs
- Giving patients control of their care
- Explaining patient responsibilities
- "We want to have a good understanding of your preferences related to discharge needs"
- Staff education on the HCAHPS survey questions

....

Conclusion

Thanks to the generous sharing of HCAHPS learning experiences and strategies by the 38 successful critical access hospital participants from across the country, the purpose of this study has been accomplished - to learn about and share high performing CAHs HCAHPS best practices. The critical access hospitals represented in this study range in average daily census from around one to over twenty, demonstrating the ability of even the smallest hospitals to not only participate in national quality improvement programs, but to stand out as leaders and make lasting contributions that will impact the hospital care provided to rural residents across the country.

This project is supported by the Health Resources and Services Administration (HRSA) of the U.S. Department of Health and Human Services (HHS) under grant number U1RRH29052, Rural Quality Improvement Technical Assistance Cooperative Agreement, $500,000 (0% financed with nongovernmental sources). This information or content and conclusions are those of the author and should not be construed as the official position or policy of, nor should any endorsements be inferred by HRSA, HHS, or the U.S. Government.

Brian Lee

MAY 0 1 2024